THE SACRED ART OF

Eating

LISA TREMONT OTA

To Suzanne ♡

Wishing you a nourishing relationship
with food through expanded love,

Lisa

Published by Sacred Exploration
ISBN: 978-0-9887266-1-1

Disclaimer

The nutrition information contained in *The Sacred Art of Eating* is general in nature, and should not be relied upon for specific medical conditions and treatments. If you need special nutrition advice or services, please contact a reliable health professional to discuss your specific situation. All efforts have been made to assure the accuracy of the information contained in this book as of the date of publication. The author disclaims all liability for any medical outcomes that may occur as a result of applying the methods suggested in this book.

www.sacredexploration.com

THE SACRED ART OF

Eating

is dedicated to
that on which we depend for life but cannot speak for itself:

the earth.

It is also dedicated to my children,

Eric and Matthew,

as an example of what it means to commit to your dreams.

CONTENTS

Foreword

Life brings us things, people, ideas, environments, circumstances and a multitude of ever changing forms. How does it happen? This question is what the mystics have been asking for eons.

My spiritual experiments in life have led me to live hundreds of nights alone in the forests all over California—by choice rather than by necessity—in order to deepen my appreciation for Earth Mother. My sadhana has led me to practice yoga for 30 years and teach it for over 20 years to thousands of students throughout the Western USA and Hawaii. My path guided me to surf hundreds of ocean waves between 2 and 20 feet pumping throughout California, North Shore Kauai, and Australia in temperatures from 58 – 84 degrees and color from crystal clear turquoise to muddy brown. I have been caretaker of two avocado orchards, grown organic gardens, and built and lived in a 200 square foot treehouse amongst 30-40 foot tall old growth avocado trees. On one of those orchards in Santa Barbara, I conducted maintenance of the land and irrigation of the avocado trees while living in an old trailer and fending off dozens of rats. While learning about service to humanity, I invited Franciscan Friar Novices to come over and glean the orchard for avocados because of their small unmarketable size (due in part to drought condition in 1994), which led to being asked to live in a mansion estate and caretake the St Anthony's Seminary behind the Queen of the Missions for the Mission Fathers for 2.5 years. I learned how original and authentic random acts of kindness, goodwill, and benevolence, however quiet and detached, sow seeds of universal flow through the energetic law of nature. This energetic flow not only satisfies survival needs, which is the first law of nature, but opens the pathway to thriving in abundance.

I have produced an international award-winning documentary feature film on rehabilitation of child soldiers once they were captured or escaped from a 20 plus years long civil war in the Pearl of Africa. The film traveled the world through ARTIVIST (social action through art) and won awards for best film in Geneva, Switzerland and Berlin, Germany, with Cinema for Peace. It also played before a full house at the United Nations General Assembly in New York City, hundreds of international diplomats and the president of the International Criminal Court at the Hague, Netherlands as well as at the High Commission on Human Rights at the Brussels, Belgium Cultural Center, and more. The creating of that film took place when I left my wilderness paradise to perform selfless service for my 84 year old uncle living in the heart of Los Angeles who wished to transition at home when I learned of his inevitable demise. I became his caregiver, nourishment, and support during his last year of life until the end came for this 70 year long master metaphysician who left his body. His wish was granted in gracious cooperation between us.

Many years before that though, I had met success through high-tech sales in corporate America but realized the limited scope of possibility in commerce, economics, politics, government, culture, and religion. My spiritual experiments led me to write, direct, and produce a yoga tutorial video called *Lifestyle of a Yogi* and later write a book on enlightenment. I have designed healing programs for a destination spa and started a healing center in Kauai as well.

How does all this stuff happen? The mystical life is way beyond the mind. It's "outside the mind" as my 82 year old retired psychiatrist friend in Ojai, California, says. By endeavoring, by engaging, by overcoming one's own fear (which is an illusion) with slow and steady effort, one transcends all obstacles on the path and becomes fearless of the unknown. One becomes courageous and curious of the unknown and bored with the known. As one continues, love in action becomes the norm attracting more and more goodness with joy, vibrancy, health, and prosperity flowing in and out from all directions. One realizes the Self within and life becomes effulgent with love and bliss. Wild animals become your friends like the wild dolphins that I have met graciously in the Australian Ocean and began surfing waves together in spontaneous, telepathic, playful bliss. Nirvikalpa Samadhi and Sahaja Samadhi take hold in the genetic structure within forever shifting the central nervous system from fear/survival to love/bliss, or sympathetic to parasympathetic state. Soul Surfers live their lives for pure aesthetic reasons—for the pure joy of it. Harmony, Simplicity, and Purity are their hallmarks.

Lisa Tremont Ota showed up in my life as a bright, angelic, joyous, benevolent life form radiating warmth and sublime, brilliant health in her aura. I was so captivated by her presence, I smiled at her to which she responded and acknowledged me. Her book, *The Sacred Art of Eating*, is chock full of wisdom, knowledge, and practical ways to obtain supreme health, avoid disease, and even reach states of transcendental bliss.

Lisa has been practicing what she teaches for a lifetime, taking the seed of her lineage and cultivating it carefully and consistently to a vibrancy few display. She has gained physical and spiritual gifts as the result of her embodied integration of living in harmony with nature and holding compassion for all. For example, she has healed herself naturally from various ailments (obsessive compulsive disorder, severe back pain, amenorrhea, human papilloma virus) even when surgery had been indicated. This ability to heal is a testimony to her deep commitment to the sacred and serves as part of her qualification as a shaman. Working with her animal spirit guides of elephant, dolphin, and dove, she has received songs in both English and Spanish which she shares in ceremony. She has also achieved unique mastery of ecstatic bliss, becoming a pioneer on the subject in the San Francisco Bay Area. She did not seek these attributes, but acquired them as the result of living a life devoted to the sacred while properly cultivating her nature as a woman.

When humanity becomes healthy enough to understand and let in the Sacred Feminine to heal the brokenness, pain and suffering from denial, deprivation and rejection of its own potential, then it will heal its long history of survival based and fear based living. Humanity is at a crossroads of realizing itself as Source or destroying itself as Source. Both she and I, being born from Cherokee People, carry on our tradition of being peace loving, cooperative and collaborative by our human nature. Once humanity overcomes fear and indifference, it will then be able to assist itself in a bona fide, legitimate, psychedelicate way through love in action. We all belong to one another and we all live in each other's hearts.

Lisa is offering the reader stepping stones to cultivate yourself to realize the zenith of your vibration. So, please value and love yourself enough to receive and apply the protocol of this book diligently to achieve the results that are now within your grasp. Lisa has "raised the bar" for us as individuals and I am grateful and humble to be her high witness. Become the alchemist within and witness yourself transform into the high conscious mammal being that is your potential. No one else can do this for you except you. You may surprise yourself to learn of the most amazing being you are becoming everyday in every way. The contribution you make to all of humanity goes out into the ethers and enhances the vibe across the planet. You are the change you seek. Upgrade yourself within and witness your dreams comes true as you believe in your essence and trust it.

Grant Inglett
Surfer, Yogi, Shaman

Acknowledgments

The gestation process for this book has been so long that it is hard to recall all the people who have played a role in birthing it. But my gratitude extends first and foremost to my parents, Jim and Bert Tremont. From babysitting my children while I taught classes to providing me with needed funds to develop my website to attending my events for the hundredth time, they have set the foundation of my commitment to this effort with their love.

With sincere gratitude, I also acknowledge:

My dear friends who have listened to me talk about this book endlessly while wondering if it would ever manifest: Tamara Effron, Kim Carpenter, Sarah Block, Cory Nickerson, Rebecca Mulqueeney, Dennis Mulqueeney, Mike Mulqueeney, Kay Ota, Donya Coffey, Lori Bassham, Stephanie Catron, Regina Veprin, Susie Pinheiro, and Jennifer Kiliany-Sears, Kevin Ota, who has a special ability to support others' dreams, and my brother, James Tremont, whose love spans decades, hemispheres, and time zones.

All those who have nurtured my relationship with the sacred, beginning with my extended family from St. Luke's Church in Foster City: the Mulqueeneys, the Igoes, the Fitzgeralds, the Maguires, the Beals, the Bunjes, the Siebers, and so many more. Your influence spans generations and is ongoing.

Reverend Matthew Fox and my dear friends from the 1996 Class of Culture and Creation Spirituality during its last year at Holy Names College, most especially Jill Martin, Ed Smith, Mel Bricker, Gina Rose Halpern (who painted the earth on my pregnant belly), and Marlene DeNardo.

My beloved colleagues and friends from the Shamanic Soul Coaching and Sacred Courtesan programs at the Institute for Integrative Studies in

Oakland, for opening up my vision to a much broader and brighter world, most especially Francesca Gentille; and DanIel Cloud, with the EnLakesh Foundation, and Pete Isaia, for deepening my experience of plant medicine used for personal and collective healing; and Grant Inglett for introducing me to velvet tickle delightful delicate heart magic and for his sincere devotion to the Goddess.

All spiritual leaders, past, present, and future: Jesus, the Buddha, Thich Nhat Hanh, the Dalai Lama, and, yes, Oprah Winfrey, plus those named and unnamed, for their great wisdom, without which I would not be who I am today. My spirit animals: the elephant for teaching me about the importance of community and displaying impressive flexibility and enormous strength; the dove for teaching me to bring love to new heights; and the dolphin for its message to communicate throughout the world.

All who have nourished my understanding and appreciation for food and nutrition: Liz Cragen, my closest colleague and friend, who recognizes my gifts, skills, and talents better than I do. My professors from the UC Berkeley School of Public Health, most especially Sheldon Margen, for his deep and everlasting wisdom surrounding the role of food on our well-being; Len Syme, who underscored my insatiable desire to understand the health-related factors that we can and cannot control; Barbara Abrams, for bringing my efforts up to date in new and exciting ways; and John Swartzberg, Editor for the UC Berkeley Wellness Letter, for providing me with great comfort through his scientific review of my work. My graduate-school classmates—Jenness Keller, Melody Steeples, Laura Martini, Laura Walter, Arnell Hinkle, and Valerie McGuire—for making our academic years and careers something more fun and valuable than words can describe. My gal pals associated with the Wellness Guide, who provided love and laughter along the way: Dale Ogar, Linda Neuhauser, Linda Blachman, Merl Ross, Gladys Fleitas, Maxine Tatmon-Gilkerson, Heidi Huhn, and Tom McNamee, for simultaneously encouraging and critiquing my book concept over hidden foodie hot spots throughout the San Francisco Bay Area.

My JuicePlus+ community, most especially Lori Bassham, my childhood and forever friend, for introducing me to the best whole-food nutrition supplement in the world; StaciJoy Ellis, for educating me all the while I educate others; Barbara Messmore, for being the best sideline buddy ever; all the representatives who have openly and enthusiastically allowed me to share my individual contribution around nutrition with their team and customers, both present and future; and those at the corporate office who have recognized my influence and patiently support me to make my dreams come true, most particularly John Blair, Karen Jones, Wendy Campbell, Kathrine Lee, and our remarkable president, Jay Martin.

Those who have paved the way and inspired me in regard to vegetarian and vegan nutrition:

John Sabate, Virginia (Ginny) Messina, Dr. Pam Popper, and Dr. Mitra Ray, and my colleagues at the American Academy of Nutrition and Dietetics Vegetarian Resource Group, and Sean Butman, who profoundly supported my own relationship with plant-based nutrition. To the Cooking with Kids Foundation for providing me with the opportunity to support their mission, most especially, Bill Durkin, for inviting me along to explore the more magical aspects of food and permaculture.

Those who have helped me take needed escape from the world of writing: my fellow *salseros* and DJs, most especially Carlitos Way and DJ Bosco; my dear friends Janis Silva and Michael Romanchak, for loving me as their own; and Phil Isaia, for providing support at just the right time in just the right ways.

All those who helped to manifest the more recent stages of my business, including the first Sacred Art of Eating Dinner Party: my colleagues and friends in BNI's Diablo Networking Circle, especially Paul Wildrick and David Shirley; April Dyer (nutrition intern) and Susie Garcia (Nutrition for Your Lifestyle), for their help in developing and analyzing the menu; Eileen Joyce Evans (What's Cookin' Personal Chef Services), for catering the event; Allison Beavers, for her event-planning expertise; Mary Redente, for her beautiful food photography; and Elise Beavers (Elise Beavers Design), for the logo and book-cover designs. Special thanks, too, to Kelly Kenny, who helped me to manifest the vision, all the while becoming a dear friend.

The numerous editors I have had the pleasure to work with over the years, including Maria Hjelm, Cher Eyecons, and Maria West, for their sincere belief in the value of my work and their remarkable patience with my perfectionism. But especially the two women without whom this book would not have seen completion: Brooke Warner, who is exactly who I needed to publish a book, and Annie Tucker, for holding my purpose sacred when weariness left me lost. And special thanks to Joel Harris for leading me to Marcus Mebes so that I can bring these words to print.

My son Eric, for being the first to give me the experience of pregnancy, birth, and motherhood. Thank you, too, for your advanced and much appreciated technological assistance and philosophical reassurances. My son, Matthew, for expanding the joy of motherhood, recognizing my work as shaman, and for his sincere and loving hugs. You two are the most direct recipients of this book's intention. And deep gratitude to my beloved, Roger, for providing me the opportunity to follow my passions and pursue my dreams, for supporting me to be my authentic self. You have shown me what makes love true.

SACRED EXPLORATION.COM

WE **ALL** have a unique, lifelong relationship with food. But for too many of us, that relationship is broken. We are born into amazing human bodies on a planet that serves up a bounty of delicious and nutritious foods, yet our disconnect with our bodies and with the earth has led us into a global food frenzy. Food can energize us and create optimal health and longevity, but it can also drain us and the planet, and lead us toward premature death and devastation.

Ask yourself the following questions: Do you eat when you aren't hungry? Are you sick and tired of being sick and tired? Do you turn to food to fill an emptiness inside you? Do you eat things that aren't even food because they're convenient? Do you find yourself dieting but gain weight instead? Do you consider how what you eat impacts the planet?

Then ask yourself what you want. A smoother complexion? Better sleep? Healing from a chronic condition, including cancer, heart disease, or an autoimmune disease? Fewer cold and flu symptoms? Shinier and stronger hair? To lose weight once and for all? To recover better from your workouts? More energy? A healthy pregnancy? An improved outlook on life? An increased level of integrity with the earth?

In both the short term and the long term, our food choices impact not only our bodies but also animals, other people, and the planet in a multitude of ways. If you answered yes to one or more of the questions above, you may find that practicing the tenets of the Sacred Art of Eating transforms your relationship with food—and your physical well-being—for the better.

❧

As with many women, my own relationship with food began at birth and then suffered. As I entered adolescence and my body matured, I got lost in an obsession about the caloric content of food. Then, when I began college, I started to ponder all the diets being promoted and our preoccupation with what we eat. *How does deciding between types of grain lead people to stand paralyzed in the cereal aisle of their local grocery store?* I wondered. *How has making choices about what to feed our bodies evolved into a nation obsessed with one fad diet after another?* I couldn't help but ponder. *And how is it possible that so many people don't have enough to eat, when the planet produces enough food for everyone?* Our overall approach to food seemed topsy-turvy to me. *Certainly, this is not what nature intended!* I surmised. All of these thoughts kick-started my personal and professional journey into the Sacred Art of Eating.

I pursued a degree in nutrition and clinical dietetics from the University of California, Berkeley, in the mid-'80s. I was fascinated by all that I learned about the role of food in the body and its ability to both harm and heal. One of my first jobs after college was as a nutritionist for the US Department of Agriculture's Special Supplemental Nutrition Program for Women, Infants, and Children (WIC), which provides supplemental foods and nutrition education for low-income pregnant, breastfeeding, and nonbreastfeeding postpartum women, and to infants and children up to age five who are found to be at nutritional risk. This experience reinforced my understanding that what we eats impacts much more than we alone. Without a doubt, the way a woman eats during pregnancy significantly impacts the health outcome of her newborn child, in both the short term and the long term.

Even after children are born, the way we purchase and prepare food and serve it to them impacts their health. Sadly, we are experiencing an alarming increase in the number of children challenged with overweight and obesity. If these trends continue, the current generation of children will be the first in history not to live as long as their parents do. This devastating and unacceptable situation is due to the fact that excess weight increases the risk of diabetes, heart disease, and cancer, all of which lead to an increased risk of premature death in children, just as they do in adults. And while it remains possible that children's life span won't shorten, their health span still will.

While I enjoyed working with individuals at WIC, I felt a sense of urgency about our nation's increasingly poor state of health, so I returned to UC Berkeley to earn a master's degree in public health nutrition. I focused on disease prevention and health promotion and used the strategies I had learned to develop wellness programs for nonprofit organizations such as the Solano County Cancer Prevention Program and the American Heart Association, and corporations including Safeway, Pacific Bell, and Advanced Fiber Communications.

In between leading dozens of nutrition-education grocery store tours, appearing on television and radio shows, and participating in community programs, I thought a lot about the role of control in how we eat. As someone with a fond appreciation of Latin culture, I took it upon myself to explore the fact that Hispanic Latinos present an epidemiological paradox in that, despite their historically lower socioeconomic status in the United States, they have lower rates of morbidity (illness) and mortality (death).

As I directed the first statewide distribution of UC Berkeley's *Wellness Guide* (*La Guía de Bienestar*) to more than one million English- and Spanish-speaking participants in California's WIC program, I began to understand how the factors we can and cannot control significantly impact our health and recognized in turn the tremendous power we have to turn our individual and communal health conditions around. Healing is within our control!

Believing that something deeper still coursed through our decisions about food, I pursued a second master's degree, in culture and creation spirituality, from Holy Names College in 1994. By strengthening my understanding of the world's religions and our cosmic interconnectedness, I more fully appreciated how what we eat impacts our local and global communities, animals, and the earth. For example, two billion people in the world are overweight or obese, another one billion people go hungry, and still another two billion people suffer from micronutrient malnutrition. We are seriously out of balance within both our national and our international communities. Further, our unhealthy relationship with food also hurts the planet; as Al Gore educated us in *An Inconvenient Truth*, we are experiencing unprecedented shifts in our global climate, many of which are influenced by the food that we eat. Animal agriculture, for example, is a major cause of environmental problems both nationally and globally, contributing to water and air pollution, water scarcity, land degradation, loss of biodiversity, and climate change.

Part Native American Cherokee, I felt a calling to study shamanism, a spiritual healing practice. Indigenous cultures around the world practice plant-based healing through a deep connection to the natural world. Shamans communicate with the sacred through spirits that exist in all natural things, including people, animals, trees, water, earth, wind, and fire. At our core essence, we are connected to everything. My learning began under the guidance of Francesca Gentille at the Institute of Integral Studies in Oakland, California. It was there that I began to understand how to work with the many parts of ourselves, both in relationship to food and in life in general, and to futher tap into the power of transformation on many levels.

While there is a dark side that we must face in order to heal, know that we are constantly undergoing transformation and that, based upon what we eat, we can experience greater and greater levels of vitality. We are not our diagnosis. Despite what medical authorities may state, we do not have cancer or heart disease or an autoimmune disease or anything else. In these cases, we have cells that are not functioning to their greatest capacity. They need help. And the ability to provide that help is within our control. Everything transforms over and over and over again. We are never the same person twice. As you practice the Sacred Art of Eating, you will experience a new you.

Early in my career, as I contemplated the

relationship between food and spirituality, I often wondered whether I was using food to help people deepen their relationship with the sacred or using spirituality to help people heal their relationship with food. Eventually, I arrived at the natural conclusion that it didn't really matter since the two are so inextricably linked. *The Sacred Art of Eating* represents my sincere hope that my combined studies and experience in the fields of nutrition and spirituality will allow me to present food to you in a way that is new and refreshing. My passion for human and planetary wholeness has led me to express myself through this book. Much of what I'll discuss is based on universal truths, but I imagine that these truths will resonate with you in a way that you haven't yet experienced and will bring you into a deeper and healthier relationship with both food and the sacred.

✍

While nothing is required (because this is a book about choices), there are several ways in which you may take part in this journey:

1. Read the book.
2. Think about the questions in the chapter-by-chapter Food for Thought section at the end of the book. Consider purchasing a journal to record your responses and any other notes of interest.
3. Practice some of the suggestions I've provided—and then practice and practice again. One of my very favorite aspects of food is that it gives us a lifetime of practice!
4. Meditate on some of the color photographs in the book. Explore what arises in your heart, mind, and body.
5. Help spread the word about what you have learned and are practicing. This book intends to generate conversation, for that is our greatest hope for increasing our collective awareness around the importance of how we eat.

The Invitation

WE BEGIN this book with an invitation to join me on a journey through the Sacred Art of Eating to illustrate the fact that we are all in a cocreative relationship with the sacred. I learned about the concept of cocreation while studying culture and creation spirituality at Holy Names College in the mid-1990s. Cocreation is an extension of intrinsic, universal laws. It is an acceptance of responsibility for creatively participating in the design of our world. Even God, or whatever name you use to refer to that energy that is both within us and greater than each of us alone, is not complete without our participation. Similarly, it's one thing for me to write this book and quite another for you to read it. As such, I greatly appreciate your contribution to this cocreative process.

Any relationship that is cocreative requires each

Please join me
in celebration of

The Sacred Art of Eating

a serious message served up within a dinner-party theme
a menu uniquely designed for your well-being and enjoyment

Earth Day

By invitation only

of the participants to have free will. When it comes to how we eat, there are multiple ways in which we can exercise our free will:

- To eat or not to eat
- What to eat
- How much to eat
- Where and when to eat
- How to eat

For now, let's explore the first three of these areas in more detail.

To Eat or Not to Eat

Without choices, people can't experience the full extent of their free will. Tragically, not everyone has the choice of whether or not to eat—a child starving in Africa, for example. But the majority of us, whether it is obvious or not, do have this choice. Many people argue that if a loving God did exist, there would be no hunger in the world, and that because hunger does exist, there must not be a God. But the truth is that there is enough food in the world to feed everyone. If those of us who have the option to practice our full range of free will were to make choices about food that supported our global community, we could end hunger. The challenge is to use our free will to make that happen. Whether others starve depends upon the choices we make. Arguably, national and international food policies limit our potential to create such a change, but politicians respond to people, particularly with

regard to how they spend their money. When it comes to food, we vote with our forks!

There are also situations in which people may voluntarily choose to restrict their food intake. For example, fasting for religious and spiritual reasons has been a part of human custom since prehistory. It is mentioned in the Bible, the Mahabharata, the Upanishads, and the Qur'an. As Gandhi demonstrated, some people restrict their food intake as a method of nonviolent resistance or political protest to draw attention to an issue in pursuit of a policy change or other goal.

Hunger strikes have historically been forcibly ended through the use of force-feeding, but, generally, eating is one of the few things authorities do not regulate. In the United States, driving alone is illegal until age sixteen and consuming alcohol is illegal until age twenty-one. But food is legal at all ages, and what we eat is one of the few things we can regulate ourselves. In a world that feels increasingly out of control, deciding what and whether to eat gives people something tangible that they can control. This is especially true for children and teens who are dependent upon their parents for most things, like food, shelter, and love.

Unfortunately, power over our food intake can fall into extreme behavior like eating disorders such as anorexia, a condition in which people attempt to maintain a weight that's far below normal for their age and height, usually by starving themselves or exercising excessively. Terry Schiavo and Karen Carpenter are two examples of women who controlled their food intake to the point of literally starving themselves to death. My best childhood friend also died prematurely from anorexia. If we do not eat, we will die.

What to Eat

Generally speaking, we also have the choice of what foods to eat. In fact, society offers us such an overwhelming number of food choices that we are often paralyzed before them. I often see people standing in the bakery section or cereal aisle of their local grocery store, unable to make a decision because there are too many choices. And because so many of these selections are void of nutrition, the "everything in moderation" mantra for a healthy lifestyle doesn't apply.

Too often, people turn to food that's fast and cheap, not food that makes them healthy. The constant availability of food in our society has desensitized us to why we need food in the first place. With grocery stores and Golden Arches on every corner, we take food for granted. We are driven by a need for speed and good taste. The nutritional value of food and its impact on the planet are factors that we often ignore. This disconnect between the purpose and the value of food is a big part of our society's current health crisis.

With junk food, we're "digesting the values that go along with it: the idea that food has to be fast, cheap, and easy; that abundance is permanent and effortless; that it doesn't matter where food actually comes from," explains noted chef and food advocate Alice Waters about the crisis of unhealthy eating we face. As a nation, we need to take back responsibility for our health and our food culture. This can mean many things, such as voting for legislature that demands appropriate food labeling, purchasing foods that support local farmers, and shifting our attitudes about the role of food in our lives.

Food is big business. The appeal of fun-tasting, convenient food is broadcast to us constantly. Corporations cut corners, modifying and processing nutrition right out of their products. Health and social responsibility are not their priorities. Sales and profits are what matter most to major grocery and restaurant chains. Even restaurants that offer healthier menu items do so because they are responding to public demand that will support their profit margin. Sure, McDonald's is conveniently located and offers inexpensive meals, and those Golden Arches may bring back fun childhood memories, but the corporation packages obesity and physical decay inside toys and kid-friendly atmospheres. The link between frequently eating fast food and obesity, high cholesterol, and feelings of depression and lethargy is well documented. Still, even though people often blame the fast-food industry for the fact that we consume so much of its product, the industry is not forcing or shoving the food down our throats. When you consume fast food—including refined carbohydrates, like pastries at your local coffee shop—you do so willingly.

In the end, every day we alone decide what to choose among the infinite number of food options. These decisions will result in whether or not we will improve or break down our health. Even an infant will spit out her food or throw it off the table if she doesn't like it. With our power to decide what we eat each morning, we have new hope for health and healing. If you want to make lasting improvements in your relationship with food, acknowledge your ability to choose what goes into your mouth.

How Much to Eat

Ideally, we make the choice to stop eating when we begin to feel full and satisfied. More often, however, we continue to eat for reasons unrelated to physiological hunger. When we are not conscious of the relationship between food and our body, we are more likely to reach for that second helping, not because we still feel hungry but because we aren't ready to leave the table. We may want something to do with our hands, or we may have the habit of eating more because the serving bowl is sitting right in front of us. Or perhaps we turn to food as a method of procrastination because we don't want to move on to our next activity. Many people also take comfort in filling an emotional sense of emptiness with the sensation of food filling their stomachs.

Brian Wansink, head of Cornell University's Food and Brand Lab, concludes that visibility and convenience are what most influence how much we eat. Imagine the food scene at an amusement park. People want to experience cotton candy, snow cones, chocolate-dipped ice cream, corn dogs, funnel cakes, kettle corn, candied apples, and so on. The constant sight of these novelties calls us to literally take it all in. In one experiment, Wansink placed candy jars of chocolate in office workers' cubicles for a month. Then, he moved the candy six feet away. Simply having the candy closer meant the office workers ate five more candies a day. At the amusement park or sporting event, you don't even have to seek the goodies out—vendors bring a wide variety of sugar- and chemical-laden food to you as you sit in your seat for the show. The sensations and tastes of these damaging foods generally seem like a prerequisite for making the event feel special.

For exa[mple]...start to...feel nervou[s]...several hours...a cup of coffe[e]...after spending...particular cow...taking an hones[t]...how your eating...impact your physica[l]...you can better reco[gnize]...the trouble spots and b[egin]...to correct them. Furth[er]...studies show that peop[le]...who keep a food journa[l]...tend to eat less food overall...(recording eating binges is painful) and better maintain weight loss.

One of the most effective techniques for developing healthier eating habits is to keep a food journal, even for a few days. Recording what, when, and how much you eat helps you to recognize how your body feels after you eat specific foods at certain times of day and in different environments.

We can also practice tuning into our bodies to get a true sense of hunger; think about a baby, who will turn its head from its mother's breast when it wants to stop nursing, or a toddler, who purses her lips or simply throws her food off the table when she has had enough. Too often, adults eat not because they are hungry but because they are bored, anxious, depressed, overwhelmed, and so on. Eating slowly and consciously helps us identify whether we *need* to eat or simply *want* to eat.

*mple, you may
realize that you
...s and anxious
... after drinking
... or ravenous
...time with a
...rker. By
...look at
...habits
...state,
...gnize
...egin
...er;
...e*

nected
nd:
n
ubt,
onger. I
d system,
e whether or
r even buy it at

umerous choices our
e at any time considers
lar option impacts us but
hers and the planet. Making a
ts us all is what one of my favorite
, Deepak Chopra, calls "spontaneous
. The decisions that we make about
among those that will determine whether we actuate this concept. The foods we buy consume have the potential to make a direct npact even on corporate giants like McDonald's and Starbucks. For example, Starbucks uses non-GMO (genetically modified organism) soy milk, and many other fast-food chains are required to list the caloric content of the foods they serve.

The earth, too, will be affected differently depending upon the foods we eat. Chopra advises the following application of the law of "karma": "Whenever I make a choice, I will ask myself two questions: 'What are the consequences of this choice that I'm making?' and 'Will this choice bring fulfillment and happiness to me and also to those who are affected by this choice?'" Applying deliberate consideration to the way we eat, we might ask ourselves, "What are the consequences of eating this particular food?" and, "Will eating this particular food bring fulfillment and happiness to me and also to those who are affected by this choice?"

Given that the average American eats three hamburgers per week, let's apply these questions to consuming a McDonald's Quarter Pounder with cheese. What are the consequences of eating this particular food? Well, we could begin with "satisfying our hunger," but we must also consider research findings that each daily increase of three ounces of red meat is associated with a 16 percent increased risk of cardiovascular death and a 10 percent increased risk of cancer death. Part of this increase is attributable to the 26 grams of mostly saturated fat, 95 milligrams of cholesterol (of which the body requires none), and 1,100 milligrams of sodium contained in the burger—that all adds up to major strain on the heart over time. Further, all this animal protein (meat and cheese) is high in sulfur, which creates the acidic environment in the body that underlies many of our chronic illnesses, like cancer and autoimmune diseases. There is some evidence, for example, that in effort to balance itself, the body pulls calcium phosphate from the bones, thereby weakening them. And then there are the antibiotics, hormones, genetically modified organisms, and pesticides that enter your bloodstream.

Now let's apply the second question: "Will eating this particular food bring fulfillment and happiness to me and also to those who are affected by this choice?" Let's presume that you experience fulfillment by eating that Quarter Pounder, but who else is affected? First and foremost, the cow that was prematurely taken from its mother and then injected with antibiotics and hormones and then slaughtered. And then there's the other cow, which was artificially inseminated in order to become pregnant, only to have her baby taken from her while she was left to produce milk for the cheese on your burger. Who else is affected by this choice? Mother Nature, who has experienced deforestation in order to provide grassland for beef cattle. Further, methane gas generated from factory livestock farming contributes more to global warming than the emissions caused by cars and other forms of transportation. How does that hamburger taste now?

CHAPTER TWO

The Guest List

EACH OF US has a unique and lifelong relationship with food; as famed chef James Beard says, it is "our common ground." Food demonstrates that, at our core, we are more similar to one another than we are different. Regardless of where we come from, what we look like, or whom we love, not one of us can live without food. It is the greatest symbolic manifestation of our interconnectedness.

When it comes to nourishing our bodies, all of us are made up of trillions of cells surrounded by two fluids: blood (which delivers oxygen and nutrients to the cells) and lymph (which helps to remove waste from the cells). Without food, none of us can do what we do. And each of us can do what we do better and best when optimally nourished. Ultimately, in my opinion, each of us is present on this planet to live our life as authentically as possible. That means doing the things that mean the most to us. Usually, those things are also the most enjoyable

and allow us to contribute to the world in our own unique way. Most of us can do more to nourish our lives through the way we eat.

Does dissatisfaction with our bodies lead us to take better care of them? The answer to that question is both yes and no. Unfortunately, sometimes people have to experience great levels of pain before they will make any changes to help heal themselves. In this way, dissatisfaction with our body and our health can lead us to take steps toward better self-care. At the same time, people who appreciate their body and their life tend to take better care of themselves.

I would like to help you appreciate your body more deeply. What do you do with your body? Following are some possibilities. You may want to write them in a journal or cut out magazine pictures of the activities you do and paste them on the cover of your journal as a reminder of all that your body does for you. Here is my list:

- Walk
- Breathe
- Eat
- Sleep
- Dream
- Read

- Hug someone
- Ski
- Study
- Laugh
- Meditate
- Pray
- Talk

- Cry
- Make love
- Vote
- Bike
- Hike
- Dance

- Cook
- Clean
- Get dressed
- Watch a movie
- Shop
- Paint
- Garden

- Write
- Sing
- Teach
- Do yoga
- Play
- Swim

Your body also does things that you don't even have to think about:

- Your heart beats between sixty and one hundred times per minute.
- Your lungs breathe in and out anywhere from fifteen to twenty-five times per minute.
- Your kidneys process about two hundred quarts of blood in order to sift out about two quarts of waste products and extra water as urine.
- Your liver filters the blood coming from the digestive tract, detoxifies chemicals, and metabolizes drugs. It also makes proteins important for blood clotting and other functions.
- Once a man and a woman have had sex, they don't have to think about anything in order for their egg and sperm to become an infant. Of course, the way a woman cares for herself during this crucial time makes a significant difference in the health outcomes of her child, but the process still occurs without her having to make any decisions.

☙

We all have relationships—with our spouse or romantic partner, with our parents and children, with our coworkers, with our friends and neighbors, and so on. But I believe that our relationship with food is one of the most intimate, intriguing, and important of all. While some people have children

and others don't, and some people get married and others don't, unlike our relationships with people, food is something that we interact with every day of our lives, as we literally take it into ourselves and it literally becomes a part of us.

Whether you believe in creationism or evolution, the human body is a sacred gift. And like a gift, it can be either opened and forgotten or opened and appreciated over time. If you treat your body well, you will have a greater ability to share your authentic self with the world. In considering what we are going to do with our gift, we seem to often overlook the fact that the only thing our bodies have to work with is what we feed them. In modern society, food is something that comes easily to us—we can grab it off a supermarket shelf, we can buy it at a fast-food drive-through, and we can get it from a vending machine. But most of that isn't even food; it's fabricated chemicals that combine to create something that tastes good and fills us up. Our constant craving for speed and convenience results in a wide range of chronic disease, including heart disease, cancer, obesity, diabetes, and autoimmune disorders.

In an attempt to control situations, our minds want to define things, especially physical conditions. Being human, we are confined to using words as a way to communicate with one another. But when you are given a diagnosis like cancer or heart disease or inflammatory bowel disease, it is important to remember that you are not that disease. It does not define you. It is merely a word that is used to represent the condition of your cells as determined by designated parameters.

One of my favorite quotes is from Helen Schucman's book *A Course in Miracles*: "Words are just symbols of symbols and thus twice removed from reality." As we move forward, I will mention disease states by name because they help define general outcomes of the body, but please remember that these terms represent conditions that may be reversible. Practice having a "don't know" attitude about your health issues, allowing for the unknown to reveal itself through positive expression, as opposed to an assumed negative condition. This approach applies to public health from the standpoint that, despite rigorous research, we cannot fully understand all of the factors that impact our health since the world is constantly changing, often in ways that our beyond our control but that impact our health. That said, we can take stock in what we do know.

For example, research confirms that what we eat is the most significant factor in both disease prevention and health promotion. For example, only 5-15 percent of all cancer cases can be attributed to genetic defects, whereas the remaining 85-95% have their roots in environmental and lifestyle factors, most especially tobacco and alcohol use, and unknown causes. Nutrition is a lifestyle factor which health organizations unanimously agree plays a highly significant role in cancer risk. Depending upon what comprises the nutrition, it can either increase or decrease the risk of cancer. After all, everything our body does for us, it does using the nutrients food provides. Depending on what we put into our mouths, we either build up or break down our body. It's time for us to take back control of our health by investing in what we feed ourselves. And what we feed ourselves is our choice—so we can choose to be and feel healthier with every sacred bite.

These choices are informed by the fact that each of us is entirely unique. Some of our differences are external, having to do with cultural or religious factors; for instance, a Seventh-day Adventist has different food preferences and practices than a kosher Jew. Some of our differences are inward, having to do with physiological factors; for example, a world-class athlete has different needs than a pregnant woman. And not only are we different from everybody else, we ourselves are never the same person twice. We move from fetus to newborn, toddler to child, and adolescent to adult. Our physical body goes through cycles of death and rebirth over time. We literally renew each cell in our body over and over again throughout our lives. We become a new person approximately every four months. This pattern offers hope to everyone who wants to improve his or her health. Since we are all different and our sense of taste changes over time, and given that what we eat is a personal choice, shouldn't our diets be just as varied?

Just as there is more than one path to connect with the sacred, there is more than one way to meet your nutritional needs. Many different kinds of healthy diets can fulfill the dietary needs of a healthy 180-pound man, for example, whether he lives in North America, Africa, or Asia. Popular diets that include certain foods and exclude others fail to support our individual preferences, so we probably won't stick with them over the long term. Similarly, you don't need to eat an orange to get a full day's supply of vitamin C. You can meet your vitamin C needs just as easily by eating a grapefruit, a serving of broccoli, or a cup of tomato soup. No one diet is ideal for everyone, yet doctors and nutrition experts continue to prescribe set eating plans. And on the most basic level, foods don't taste the same to everyone, just as they taste differently to all of us at different times of our lives, so one person's favorite food may taste foul to someone else.

The way we experience foods differently came across strongly to me while observing a classroom discussion of third through fifth graders. To explain the difference between fact and opinion, the instructor started a debate between two groups of students with the statement "Parents should force their kids to eat vegetables."

One student asserted, "Parents shouldn't force you to eat vegetables, because some vegetables are gross, like peas and asparagus." This caused quite a reaction from the other camp, which claimed that peas and asparagus taste delicious. Even among elementary-school children of similar ages, the same foods can taste appetizing or disgusting. It's fun to see who does and doesn't like cilantro, for example. It seems as if people either love it or hate it.

Scientists are also learning more about the striking diversity of taste sensitivity. Just as flavor is more than taste, taste is more than a genetic impulse. Some people are supertasters who rarely eat leafy greens because the taste is too strong for them, while other people can barely detect bitter flavors. People's food preferences and eating habits are also based largely on what they grew up eating and even on what their mothers ate during pregnancy. Children who are breastfed, for example, tend to be more open to various flavors and thus eat a wide variety of foods. Those who are formula-fed, on the other hand, tend to have a much more limited palate, presumably because they were exposed to the same taste over and over again.

If a child rejects a particular food, don't give up! Given that our taste buds change five to seven times over our lives, it is important to reintroduce healthy foods to a child at least a dozen times before you give up on the child's liking that particular food. However, contrary to the teacher's statement in the classroom exercise I observed, forcing children to eat vegetables over the long term can cause negative associations that may last a lifetime. Again, given that food is one of the few things that young children can control (how much and whether or not to eat), it is important that they be allowed to make decisions about it for themselves.

✂

The word "beautiful" is meant as a positive description of a person, animal, object, natural force, feeling, or state. But depending on how we feel about ourselves and how we feel seen by others, it can conjure up different feelings (appreciation, sadness, envy). Why does "beautiful" so often describe how a person compares with a narrowly defined ideal of what he or she should look like? Why is it physical? Why is it so limited that most people don't think they should be called "beautiful"?

The Bible speaks of true beauty as inner beauty that comes from a gentle, loving soul:

> *What matters is not your outer appearance—the styling of your hair, the jewelry you wear, the cut of your clothes—but your inner disposition. Cultivate inner beauty, the gentle, gracious kind that God delights in.*
> —The Message, 1 Peter 3:3,4

Many of us—especially women, including me—experience resentment and frustration toward our bodies. All our lives, we have been bombarded with images of what women should look like. We struggle in adolescence to meet an ideal, or we hate ourselves for not being able to meet it. Even the young women who come closest to resembling an ideal usually feel the weight of their imperfections, thinking they need to change their bodies so they can be more acceptable and ultimately lovable. But our bodies are not who we are. They are vehicles that we need to move through life. True beauty is unfading through the years. This means that our graying hair and balding patterns, growing waistlines, and wrinkling skin don't detract from our beauty. Can you look in the mirror, into your own eyes, and see the loving soul inside? That is your real beauty. I'm not saying it's easy or natural to do. In my experience, it's not. But I do believe it is true and worth practicing.

✂

We also obsess over our weight and dress size. We worry when we gain weight and fall into depression when we can't seem to lose it. Women especially, but men also, feel that our weight reflects our value. But what is your *true* value? Do you like your friends more if they weigh 120 pounds instead of 220 pounds? Probably not. You probably like them for their personality, which does not change.

Your weight isn't what makes you valuable, but you may not believe this unless you do some work to reframe how you see your body and your own beauty. Taking care of your body is about loving yourself and respecting your body as a gift. However, does weight loss benefit your health? In most cases, yes. Scientific evidence overwhelmingly suggests that most people cannot experience vibrant health and reduced risk of disease while being obese. The good news is that if you are overweight, losing even 5 percent of your total weight reduces your risk of cardiovascular disease and diabetes. Further, most people seem to be happier and more vibrant when carrying less weight.

However, we know change can be difficult, and that's why most people never change their eating habits. Most often, people become willing to try something new only when their failing body forces them to do so—such as when they are at risk of being bedridden with a serious physical problem, like a cancer diagnosis.

For me, getting out of the weight-obsession cycle was about wanting not to get up every morning feeling as if I had to make up for my unhealthy choices the night before. I wanted to feel good physically *more* than I wanted to overeat the night before. Every choice we make is based on what we want most. If what I want most is to have the chocolate cake tonight, despite knowing that I will wake up the next day feeling tired and mentally foggy, then I will choose to eat the cake.

What do you want most of all? Do you want to feel healthy and energetic, with a strong body that you feel good about? Or do you want to eat anything offered to you or that you have the urge to eat? What will you do with the body you have been given? Will you choose foods that will give you energy to be happy and clear-minded, or will you choose foods that will leave you feeling sluggish and disappointed in yourself hours later? Every day, you get to choose again to eat things that will nourish your body and nurture your ability to put the maximum effort into achieving your life goals.

❧

No one really likes to diet. When people go on a diet, part of them usually "dies" in the process. It may be the part that likes to eat out with friends, or the part that likes bananas even though "white foods" are forbidden on the diet, or the part that is hungry but doesn't get to eat because the diet calls for severe calorie restriction or insists that you eat at specific times of the day. It is easy to spend thousands of dollars on weight loss and get no results, or even gain weight. That's because *permanent* weight loss requires people to adopt eating and exercise habits that they can practice in the long term. Most fad diets promise quick results; every time you go online, you are likely to see an advertisement for a weight-loss secret. The only real secret is that most of these so-called miracle cures don't work.

In 2004, the Federal Trade Commission launched Operation Big Fat Lie, a nationwide law-enforcement sweep against six companies making false weight-loss claims in national advertisements.

The following slogans guarantee that a diet is a fad:

- Lose weight without diet or exercise.
- Lose weight no matter how much of your favorite food you eat.
- Lose weight permanently. Never diet again.
- Block the absorption of fat, carbohydrates, and/or calories.
- Lose thirty pounds in thirty days.
- Everybody will lose weight.
- Lose weight with a miracle diet patch or cream.

Operation Big Fat Lie promoted the commission's goals to stop deceptive advertising and get refunds for consumers harmed by untruthful weight-loss advertisers, as well as to encourage media outlets not to run ads that make false weight-loss claims. The commission also informed the public about being wary of companies promoting weight loss without diet or exercise. While we may learn something from the myriad fad diets out there, most of them aren't fun, sexy, or even healthy. It's time to rethink the way we change our bodies for good.

&

I have found that when I educate and motivate others toward better health, I eat better myself. I also find that the people who adopt the habits I am promoting end up supporting me to practice those behaviors. This exemplifies a spiritual truth that we keep what we have by giving it away. At our deepest core, we are all connected, so by giving to others, we give to ourselves. Given that we are in a lifelong relationship with food, we need lots and lots of reminders to eat well. Relying on our bodies to inform our decisions about food is not enough to nourish them optimally—for example, by the time you are thirsty, your body is already dehydrated. One of the goals of *The Sacred Art of Eating* is to remind you of what you already know on a deep, unconscious level but have perhaps lost, forgotten, hidden, or denied.

The Sacred Art of Eating does not detail foods that you must eat or foods that you must avoid. Where is the power of personal choice in that? Instead, I give you guiding principles on how to eat for our individual, communal, and environmental well-being. Because we all live in human bodies, these guidelines are similar for all of us yet offer the freedom to choose the foods we each prefer, because no two of us need to eat exactly the same thing. What unites us is the inseparable connection between food and spirituality. We are spiritual beings living in human bodies that are dependent upon food for life, and we are all invited to the table in celebration of our relationship with food and with the sacred, no matter where we are in those relationships now.

CHAPTER THREE

Your Hostess

IT IS MY great pleasure to be your hostess for this journey into the Sacred Art of Eating. My mission is to educate and inspire you toward greater levels of human wholeness. As such, it may be helpful for you to have insight into my thought processes about food and how it serves as an amazing example of our relationship with the sacred.

As I have mentioned, we are in a cocreative relationship with the sacred. This concept involves the idea that we both have control and do not have control over different aspects of our lives. My personal understanding of this concept began at an early age, due to the fact that I suffered from obsessive-compulsive disorder, or OCD.

One. Two. Three. Four.
One. Two. Three. Four.
One. Two. Three. Four.
One. Two. Three. Four.
Oh, how hard it can be to get out the door.

OCD is an anxiety disorder that causes people to experience obsessive, unwanted thoughts and to compulsively and repeatedly perform behaviors or rituals. It could manifest itself as frequent hand washing, repeatedly sitting down in and getting up from a chair, checking buttons on clothes, or rewriting words over and over until the paper tears from constant pressure. Such rituals take up a great deal of time and can mildly or severely limit one's ability to perform important tasks at home, school, and work.

For me, this crazy behavior began at about the age of seven—considered the age of consciousness, when children begin to understand cause-and-effect relationships: Scream and someone comes running. Touch a hot stove and get burned. Give someone a hug and see him or her smile.

I began to realize that there were consequences to my actions. I don't mean to offend anyone who has or has had this disorder by using the word

I don't really remember refusing to go to school. I was a good student, I loved learning, and I wanted to do well, but all along the way there, I would perform rituals to protect the people I loved. It makes sense that most of this happened in my head: people couldn't see what was going on in there, and that made these behaviors easier to hide. But I busied myself with physical rituals, too. Every morning after my dad left the house to go to work, I would run to the window in my upstairs bedroom to watch his baby-blue VW Bug make a right turn around the corner and on toward his workday, when I wouldn't see him anymore. Somehow, my ability to do that conferred some level of protection upon him.

Now, I can see that my belief may have come partly from being raised in the Catholic church, where ritual, as "crazy," but that's how it felt to me.

While I did believe in Santa Claus, I wasn't superstitious. I knew that my thoughts and acts were senseless, time-consuming, and unnecessary. I knew it, but I couldn't control them. I was *compelled* to do these things again and again and again. I *had* to. Inside my head, I heard my own voice screaming, *I can't help it!*

with all world religions, plays a highly significant role. I was a child. I had a good home life. I had no reason not to believe whatever I was presented with. So, having done my part to "protect" my father and ensure his safe return home, I would continue with my own day—filled with oh so many things to do.

My parents had a cabin up in California's Gold

Country that we loved to visit, but getting there required driving across the San Mateo–Hayward Bridge. I remember having to tap my way all across it because I had an irrational fear that we might drive off that bridge. It wasn't that I didn't trust my dad's driving; it was more of a feeling that something beyond my control could take control, unless I influenced it with my actions. I probably couldn't have said so at the time, but I see now that I was deeply and frantically afraid of death. Like all children, I grew to understand that death exists: flowers die, bugs die, and, yes, Grandma and Grandpa and even Mommy and Daddy would die. I would die, too. Even as a little girl who believed in heaven, I found death unbearably sad. I treasured life so much that I didn't want to lose it.

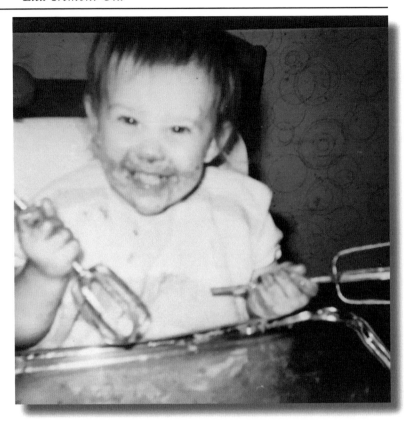

Oftentimes, I repeated actions until they felt "just right," such as going back and forth through a door, or up and down stairs, or rereading and rewriting school assignments. But mostly for me it was a lot about the number four. When sitting on an airplane, for example, I would have to cross myself four times, or four-times-four times, or even four-to-the-fourth-power times. There was no mathematical end to this madness. Sometimes I would use my eyes to capture four words in the middle of a sentence without seeing the first and last word of the line. Crazy!

Why four? Perhaps because there were four people in my immediate family, or because I was raised Catholic, and to begin praying I would cross myself, touching upon four points—because there are four elements: earth, air, fire, and water? Because there are four directions: north, south, east, and west? I don't really know.

Decades later, it's easy for me to remember how I began my prayers, because I always began them in exactly the same way:

In the name of the Father, the Son, and the Holy Spirit, amen.
Dear God, please bless my mom, dad, me, and my brother.
Please keep my mom, dad, me, and my brother safe from harm of any kind, type, assortment, or variation.

I laugh at myself now. I think I might have made a good lawyer if I'd ever thought I had the desire or the ability. What term might I have added to my prayer if my number had been five? Hmm . . . "classification"? That could work.

It's still hard to imagine what a burden this must have been on my parents if they had any idea of what was going on with me. Fortunately, they didn't. Of course, now that I am a mother myself, I can't imagine not knowing such a thing about my own child, but I performed all my rituals in secret, to the best of my ability. My mother didn't know. My father didn't know. My brother didn't know. My teachers didn't know. The clergy didn't know. My friends didn't know. Except for God, I was alone with myself in this state of disorder. And while I knew that there was something else that was aware of my situation, it wasn't something that I could see, hear, smell, feel, or taste. I didn't want anyone to know that I was a fraud.

I realize now that having OCD didn't mean that the things I was then weren't true: that I loved to dance, that I wanted to be a third-grade teacher, and that I was a good friend. It just meant that I was all those things and crazy, too. This is what I call the "both/and" principle. Understanding it can ease a lot of tension.

❦

There was one time when I tried to "come out" about my issue (which, again, I didn't have a name for). I was in a fabric store one afternoon and, after having felt compelled to touch the various rolls of material (or "tamerial," as I called it then), said, "Mom, when you were little, did you play counting games?"

"Counting games?" she repeated. "Well . . . I can remember when my brothers and I would go on long car trips and we would count the cows we saw on our side of the road as we drove. If we passed a graveyard, the person on that side of the car would lose all of their cows. At the end of the trip, whoever had the most cows won."

I knew that type of counting was not at all the kind that consumed me. Ask an indirect question, you get an indirect answer. But at least this vague question would allow me to get away with my obsessions a little longer without anybody's knowing.

I didn't blame my parents for not seeing it, not then and not now. Unlike it is today, OCD was not featured on the cover of *Family Circle* magazine or discussed on *Oprah*. Pediatricians didn't know to ask probing questions. And, most significantly, my ego was big enough to keep me from looking as crazy as I felt. I was happy, earned straight A's, and was crowned homecoming queen. On the outside, everything seemed just fine. Sure, some of my friends noticed something odd here and there, but I didn't do anything in public to such an extreme that it seemed pathological. With my close friends, it was just enough to be cute. *Fine*, I thought. *Better cute than crazy.*

I remember one day, when I was in about the sixth grade, a friend came over to hang out. I don't remember what we were talking about, but it didn't take long before we picked up on each other's obsession. We had the same problem and, for the first time, realized that we were not alone in it. We fell to the ground and literally rolled around on the bathroom floor, laughing hysterically until we cried. We shared a profound relief that each of us was not the only one in the world with this problem. But knowing that someone else had it didn't make it go away.

When my protective rituals began to require other people's participation—first my brother's, then my boyfriend's—I knew I was in trouble. *How can I make my brother knock back on the wall in the way I want him to? And how can I make my boyfriend kiss me four times?* Of course he did and was pleased to do so at first, but quite quickly he became annoyed and I felt desperate. How could I make someone do something just because I asked him or her to? I realized that I could control only myself—not others or their circumstances.

❧

Even if my parents had known what was going on, saying "stop it" is completely meaningless to children with OCD. Believe me, those children want nothing more than to be able to "stop it"— but they can't. And while there is no cure for OCD, it can now be treated successfully with cognitive behavioral therapy, antidepressants, or a combination of the two. Too often, however, in my opinion, the medications are given first, and oftentimes to the exclusion of therapy. And while I will not disagree that medications can be helpful, I am very wary of them since my own healing did not require them. I imagine that there are some who suffer or have a child who suffers with this disorder who may want to close this book now. Indeed, some have cautioned me about sharing my experience of healing to begin with, since what worked for me may not work for others. That may be true. On the other hand, I did not have access to anything that anybody else does not have access to. In fact, I am sure that I had less help than any child or adult suffering today.

You see, once I realized that my ability to control others was limited at best, I saw the senselessness of it all more easily. I began to see it everywhere. If I wanted my mom to stop smoking, she would have to be the one to make that happen. If someone wanted to think about me in ways that made me feel uncomfortable, there was nothing I could do to stop him. There was no way to guarantee much of anything having to do with anyone else. This understanding that I couldn't control other people, combined with the sheer exhaustion that my behavior caused me, felt worse than what might happen if I abandoned the disorder.

This was a crucial turning point that taught me one of life's most helpful lessons: we make choices based on what we want most. In this case, I wanted to be relieved of my self-imprisonment more than I wanted the (false) guarantee that no harm would come to those I loved. So one night, after reciting my ritualistic prayer, I told God that I didn't care anymore if giving up my irrational counting behaviors meant that my mom, my dad, my brother, or I would die. I was willing to give it all up. It was a wholehearted and complete surrender. The very thing that I feared most—death—was the thing that I was willing to take on, if required, to relieve myself of this burden.

Well, I guess God did not want me to suffer, for I was relieved. You might imagine that I emerged from that darkness somewhat gradually, but I remember its being rather immediate. I had released control and healed as a result. And, remarkably, nearly thirty-five years later, my mom, my dad, my brother, and I are all still alive and well—even without my having to perform my rituals. Imagine that!

Why do I share this story with you, and what does it have to do with eating well? I share it because, as with most painful journeys, it ultimately conveys a lesson that outweighs all the suffering. I released control that I never really had in the first place. I experienced what it meant to surrender, and I did it by making a conscious decision. I was in control of my decision to release control. But then a new obsession came over me.

Don't we all have fond memories of food? I remember family reunions in Missouri with more than ten types of homemade pie for dessert; visits to my grandfather's farm, where he hand-cranked milk fresh from the cow into ice cream; and stops at Dairy Queen, Foster's Freeze, and McDonald's on our way up to the cabin. One of the most significant foods in my life has been See's Candies. My father was the treasurer of that company starting when I was one year old, which is why I like to say that I was nearly conceived in chocolate, and why I'm so sweet. (Or would it be bittersweet?) In any case, I grew up with the real thing, and the closest thing to a behind-the-scenes pass to Willy Wonka's Chocolate Factory. When my dad came home with empty barrels that had been used to transport chocolate, my brother and I would sit inside them, taking in the aroma, before they became our garbage cans or storage containers. See's Candies were a part of all of our family gatherings and holidays: heart-shaped boxes for Valentine's Day, chocolate eggs in our Easter baskets, and Irish potatoes on St. Patrick's Day. We didn't go on a camping trip where there weren't sugar sticks and lollipops to enjoy.

But things grew challenging when we received boxes and boxes of candy for donation to various organizations. All I had to do was go into the garage and open one of the many boxes there to find, for example, sixty pieces of Scotchmallow. This was temptation at its best for an adolescent girl, and I was not good at resisting it. My growing habit of pigging out was not restricted to See's Candies, either (they were probably just the most delicious). There was the time, too, when my boyfriend and I had just broken up, and after I got out of his car and into the house, I made my way to the kitchen and proceeded to eat nearly all the brownies that my mom had baked earlier that day. Once I got started, it seemed I couldn't stop. Of course, I was feeding my sadness and confusion. Overeating was a simple way to numb any feeling that was uncomfortable. And while the blood rushed to my intestinal system, away from my brain, and I was able to fall asleep, I woke up the next morning feeling awful. This event began an overeating-and-dieting cycle that would last for years to come.

&

My mom, along with most women in the 1960s and '70s, did a respectable job of providing well-balanced meals for our family, which in those days meant following the US Department of Agriculture's Basic Four food groups (1956–1992).

As convenience-based living grew in popularity, names like Betty Crocker, Aunt Jemima, and Sara Lee joined family tables all across the country. I was a skinny child, so the nutrient content of these foods didn't faze me at all, until my body matured and started to gain weight in ways that made me wonder if I could "keep up" with the models on magazine covers. Meanwhile, my mom and most of her friends routinely went on and off Weight Watchers and other diet plans. *Family Circle*, *Woman's Day*, and *Ladies' Home Journal* featured one diet or another in each issue.

Now my counting turned to calories. Of course, this was an entirely different type of counting than when I had OCD, but the obsession felt familiar. However, unlike with OCD, I wasn't alone in this area by any means, as the vast majority of young women were, and still are, at least somewhat obsessed with food and their weight. This makes sense to me, given that, again, most of us want to feel in control of our lives.

જી

When I was a child, I always wanted to be a third-grade teacher. I remember my brother saying that I never wanted to play house, but rather school, and that I always wanted to be the teacher. In 1982 I headed off to UC Santa Barbara, where I began learning how to teach elementary math using colored blocks. But when it came time to declare a major, I didn't understand that I could major in just about anything and still get my teaching credential upon graduation. So I walked around campus for a couple of days, wondering what other career options I had. (Amazing how a misunderstanding can so dramatically alter one's course in life.) That's when I noticed a sea of female students like me, wearing boxer shorts to hide their freshman ten—the ten pounds that young women tended to gain when they left home and went off to college in those days, and that today is called the freshman fifteen.

While I was in college, I often wondered, How can this be right? How can it be that we are born into these amazing human bodies on a planet that provides nutritious food for us to eat, and yet we are destroying ourselves with what and how we eat? And thus began my journey into the Sacred Art of Eating. After two years at UCSB, I transferred to UC Berkeley to pursue an undergraduate degree in nutrition and clinical dietetics. It was there that I learned all the wonderful things that good food can do for the body. I learned what nutrients in food lead to heart disease, diabetes, and cancer, and about the prescriptive diets that help to control and potentially reverse those diseases.

I also had the good fortune to be admitted

into a specialized program called the Coordinated Program in Dietetics (CPD). There were only ten participants, and we had the unique opportunity to complete our internship requirements during the program itself. The CPD allowed us to study a particular health issue—cardiovascular disease, for example, commonly called heart disease—and then work with patients diagnosed with that disease.

I will never forget having ten minutes to educate a sixty-five-year-old man about how to change a lifetime of eating habits while he lay in his hospital bed after having triple-bypass surgery.

"Can I have an omelet with sausage and hash browns on Sundays after church?" he asked.

"Once in a while," I answered.

"What about a hot dog and beer when I'm at the baseball game with my grandson?" he continued. "What about cake and ice cream at my grandson's birthday party? Can I stop for a burger and fries on my road trips to the mountains?"

This line of questioning helped me to realize two things: 1) The familiar and generally accepted advice "everything in moderation" just doesn't work anymore. There is simply too much "everything" for that to be wise; 2) I wanted to be on the side of prevention. I understood that it is much easier to develop healthy eating habits as a child than it is to try to reverse a lifetime of poor eating habits in a short period of time.

Coincidentally, as I approached graduation, my dad underwent double-bypass surgery at the early age of forty-eight. Bypass surgery is usually performed when someone's arteries are clogged because of a diet that leads to plaque formation and inflammation. Fortunately, I had more than ten minutes to spend with him. I educated my parents about how to improve his diet and handed them a copy of *Dr. Dean Ornish's Program for Reversing Heart Disease*. My mom was quick to change her way of shopping and cooking, and as a result, my dad has far surpassed the odds and is alive and well at the time of this book's publication. So one of the most significant points to reiterate here is that food can either kill us or heal us. It is the only thing our bodies have to work with, and yet we take that fact for granted, even as many major diseases, including diabetes, heart disease, and cancer, are caused primarily by what we put in our mouths.

❧

After I received my master's degree in public health nutrition—which taught me about the challenges of changing human behavior, particularly in regard to eating, and theories about how to accomplish it—I developed wellness programs for corporations and nonprofit organizations. During this time, I furthered my thoughts about the relationship between food and spirituality, with emphasis on health-related risk factors that we can and cannot control. Risk factors we *can* control include:

- Diabetes
- Obesity
- Diet
- High blood pressure
- High blood-lipid levels
- Smoking
- Lack of exercise
- Stress

Risk factors we *cannot* control include:

- Age
- Gender
- Genetics

Among the above factors that are within our control, diet plays a leading role in the outcome of our health. Any relationship that is cocreative requires that each of the participants have free will. As a reminder, when it comes to how we eat, there are several areas in which we can exercise this free will:

- Whether or not to eat
- What to eat
- How much to eat

For a review, please refer to chapter 1. In summary, we live among factors that we both can and cannot control. My experience with OCD taught me how to use my free will to release control and trust the unknown. My obsession with food taught me how to use my free will to influence factors that are within my control and trust the known. While eating well involves working with both the known and the unknown, this book focuses primarily on using our free will to manage those factors that are within our control.

It is only when we have the courage
To face things exactly as they are,
Without any self-deception or illusion,
That a light will develop out of the events,
By which the path to success
May be recognized.

—*I Ching*, Hexagram 5, Hsu, Waiting
(Nourishment)

SACRED EXPLORATION.COM

CHAPTER FOUR

Eating for Our Individual, Communal, and Environmental Well-Being

BEFORE WE EXPLORE the steps we can take to bring harmony to the global table, we must become aware of our circumstances. It is no secret that we have a health care crisis on our hands, though we may choose to ignore that fact. Throughout *The Sacred Art of Eating*, I refer to the benefits of eating for our individual, communal, and environmental well-being. Ideally, this concept of eating for reasons beyond yourself will become deeply ingrained in you (as it has for me). The first step toward healing is to take an honest look at how our current eating patterns are impacting both us and others.

Individual Well-Being

The United States has undergone a continuous period of health improvement that is unparalleled in history. Just one hundred years ago, the average life expectancy in the United States was forty-six years of age for men and forty-eight years of age for women. Today, based on the latest data from the National Center of Health Statistics, life expectancy is seventy-eight years. Historically, people share a desire to live a long life, even forever. In the early sixteenth century, for example, Juan Ponce de León searched high and low for the Fountain of Youth. Novels like Jonathan Swift's *Gulliver's Travels*, Bram Stoker's *Dracula*, and Douglas Adams's *The Hitchhiker's Guide to the Galaxy* carried themes about living forever. But in each case, problems with immortality exist. Even in *Peter Pan*, Wendy and her brothers have the option to stay young forever but return home instead to grow up (and eventually die). The Bible makes numerous references to the notion that God rewards those in his favor with long life but at the same time makes it clear that our bodies are only temporary: "Then the Lord said, 'My Spirit will not contend with man forever, for he is mortal; his days will be a hundred and twenty years.'"

We now know that we can live significantly longer with better health. The advancing field of epigenetics ("above genetics") helps us recognize that we are not necessarily set up to experience the same outcomes as our ancestors, despite our similar genes. Epigenetics studies the factors—including diet, exercise, exposure to toxins, and even our attitude—that impact gene expression. It also considers the electromagnetic impact of quantum physics, which helps explain the "placebo effect" in which people's health improves simply because they think they have taken a medicine that will bring healing, when in fact they have not. As Richard Rudd, developer of the Gene Keys, a guide to unlocking the higher purpose hidden in our DNA, says, "What all of this means is that you can never be a victim of your DNA. Neither can you be a victim of fate. You can only be a victim of your attitude. Every thought you think, every feeling you have, every word you utter, and every action you take directly programs your genes and therefore your reality."

Whether or not you experience the same poor health outcomes as your grandparents depends much more on your lifestyle practices than on the fact that you share the same genes. This concept is most visible when we consider that a true genetic mutation generally occurs over multiple generations, yet chronic diseases are increasing at a rate that an increased number of people with a gene for those particular disease states cannot substantiate. This pattern indicates that something beyond genetics is at play, and those factors, especially diet, are largely within our control. You are not your mother's genes!

Today, we experience greater incidence of disease due to malnutrition from overconsumption of highly processed manufactured foods than from dietary deficiencies. As people's weight increases, so does their risk of cardiovascular (heart) disease, the leading cause of death among both men and women in the United States. What you eat directly impacts your risk for heart disease. One in three adults has heart disease, but most people it kills never knew they had it. We don't often realize that someone is suffering with heart disease until he or she drops dead and an autopsy is performed.

I often think of a story that my holistic-nurse friend, StaciJoy Ellis, tells about when she used to work in the emergency room on holidays. "Sure enough," she says, "at about four or five o'clock, people start rolling into the ER with chest pains." That's because we tend to eat a lot of food, including high-fat foods, on significant holidays. Several hours after a high-fat meal, however, our arteries constrict for four to six hours, thereby reducing blood flow, and thus oxygen, to the body. Not enough oxygen to the brain can result in a stroke; not enough oxygen to the heart can result in a heart attack. A

dear friend of mine in her late sixties died of a heart attack in her sleep the night following Easter Sunday 2013. While I cannot say with any certainty what caused the heart attack, it is a reasonable notion that a scrumptious day of eating may have played a role. As one American dies of cardiovascular disease every thirty-seven seconds and we know diet is a leading cause of this disease, doesn't it make sense to change the way we eat?

Besides increasing the risk of hypertension (high blood pressure), high blood cholesterol, and high triglycerides, all of which increase the risk of CAD, excess weight also increases the risk of diabetes, autoimmune disorders, and nearly all leading types of cancer. Studies that compare weight with cancer deaths have found that the higher the weight, the higher the risk. Given that 65 percent of the US population is overweight or obese, our individual and collective health status is a serious concern.

According to the Centers for Disease Control's (CDC's) 1999–2014 National Health and Nutrition Examination Survey, more than two out of three American adults are overweight or obese. Again, we are constantly transforming, and the direction in which we transform is dependent primarily upon what we eat. If we eat poorly, we will transform toward poor health. If we eat optimally, we will transform toward optimal health. As you read in chapter 3, my father underwent double-bypass surgery at an early age. But because he radically changed the way he eats, he far surpassed the odds and in 2014 is seventy-six and going strong. Our cells turn over constantly. Change how you nourish your body, and change your life for good! As you will learn, the approach to eating that I recommend will help you to lose weight and maintain your weight loss permanently.

Communal Well-Being

The most significant and valuable extension of our individual selves is our community, composed most especially of our children.

I was pregnant with my first child in 1996. While it certainly had its challenges, I absolutely loved the experience. As a nutritionist, I already followed a generally healthy diet. But as a pregnant woman, I began to eat even better. As it turns out, I wasn't alone: pregnant women are the healthiest of any subpopulation group. Why? Because through compassion for their unborn child—because they care more about the life growing within them than they do about their own—most women take better care of themselves during pregnancy than at any other time in their lives. That's good news, since what a woman eats during pregnancy has both short- and long-term consequences for her baby's health.

Still, once children are born, they become vulnerable to all kinds of outside factors that can negatively affect their health. For example, a May 2012 *Newsweek* cover showed a baby crying, "When I Grow Up, I'm Going to Weigh 300 Lbs. Help!" While life expectancy during our particular historical period has reached record levels, this trend is not expected to be sustainable if current patterns toward overweight and obesity continue. The prevalence of obesity among school-age children and adolescents more than tripled between 1970 and 2010, from less than 5 percent to 18 percent. When I was getting my degree in nutrition and clinical dietetics, we spoke of type 2 diabetes as "adult-onset diabetes." That term is no longer used, because too many children now have type 2 diabetes. "Even if the life span of children doesn't shorten, their health span will if things don't turn around very soon," declares Dr. David Katz, director of the Yale-Griffin Prevention Research Center. In addition to increasing the risk of disease and premature death, being overweight also places a tremendous unnecessary psychological burden on children.

Who else is impacted by our trends toward overweight and obesity? According to the report "The Surgeon General's Call to Action to Prevent and Decrease Overweight and Obesity," the medical and related costs of obesity in the United States in 2000 were more than $117 billion. The CDC reports that in one two-year period, US taxpayers spent $127 million on hospital costs associated with caring for overweight children and adolescents. Companies also struggle to cover health care costs for their employees. According to the CDC, each year more than $33 billion in medical costs and $9 billion in lost productivity are attributed to heart disease, cancer, stroke, and diabetes. In 2000, California alone paid nearly $25 billion in health care costs and lost productivity because of overweight, obesity, and physical inactivity. More than a quarter of all Americans age

seventeen to twenty-three are unqualified for military service because of their weight—a statistic that could impact our national security. In 2013, the Coast Guard assumed that the average boat passenger weighs 185 pounds, up from the 160 pounds in place since 1960.

Internationally, one theme we see over and over is how the populations of other countries are slowly but surely expanding their girth by becoming more like us! First it was Europe, then Australia, and now India. I remember a 2005 headline that read: "Obesity Spreads Across the Atlantic to Europe: Weighty Problem Now as Big as in US." How can we possibly feel good about that? Do these reports make us proud to be American? I hope not! Either people immigrate to the United States and begin to adopt our lifestyle, or corporations bent on building

new markets push our convenience-based lifestyle onto other countries, leading those places' citizens to suffer the same physical fate as our own. It sounds grim, but recognizing the truth is an important step toward positive behavioral change. According to a November 2014 report by the McKinsey Global Institute, obesity is a critical global issue; more than 2.1 billion people—nearly 30 percent of the global population—are overweight or obese. While obesity should be preventable, if its current trajectory continues, estimates indicate that almost half of the world's adult population will be overweight or obese by 2030—and other reports suggest that statistic is conservative.

While two billion people in the world are overweight or obese, one billion hunger for food and two billion people have micronutrient malnutrition. In 2010, 17.2 million American households, about one in seven, were food-insecure, the highest number ever recorded in the United States. The Academy of Nutrition and Dietetics (AND) defines food insecurity as limited or intermittent access to nutritionally adequate, safe, and acceptable foods accessed in socially acceptable ways. The AND contends, "Access to food is a basic human need and fundamental right . . . and . . . it is unwise and shortsighted to allow this serious, yet avoidable, public health issue to continue."

As distressing as hunger is in the United States, its prevalence is greater and its consequences even more severe in developing countries. One of the primary factors contributing to the increasing scarcity of food in the world is a rapidly expanding population, which brings an additional 219,000 people to feed at the global dinner table each night. The majority of these new people live in developing countries. The "poorest of the poor" are usually female, due to the fact that many countries continue to undervalue women and therefore provide girls with poorer diets and fewer opportunities. Malnourished girls become malnourished mothers who give birth to low-birth-weight infants—continuing the cycle of hunger, malnutrition, and poverty. Meanwhile, an estimated one-third of the nine billion people expected to inhabit the planet by 2050 are moving up the food chain, consuming more meat, milk, and eggs.

When I was a child, I often visited my grandfather's farm in Missouri, where he grew a variety of produce items, like corn, squash, and beans, and also raised chickens for their eggs and cows for their milk. (He even named one of his calves after me.) But today's unsurpassed demand for animal products means farms must maximize their efficiency and reduce their costs in ways that are sometimes cruel and inhumane.

Dairy cows, for example, are repeatedly impregnated in order to produce milk. If that were done to a human, it would be called rape! Further, up to 80 percent of all antibiotics sold in the United States are used in industrial animal confinements for chicken, beef, and hogs, not to treat disease but to make the animals grow faster. Young calves grow so fast that they can't even hold themselves up! These antibiotics are used in efforts to control the increasing threat of disease caused by overcrowded and unsanitary conditions on factory farms. Of course, this circles back to our individual well-being, in that our consumption of animal products has led to a steady rise in antibiotic-resistant bacteria that no longer respond to antibiotics intended to treat disease in humans.

According to the landmark "Antibiotic Resistance Threat Report," published by the CDC in 2013, two million American adults and children become infected with antibiotic-resistant bacteria each year, and at least twenty-three thousand die as a direct result of infections. Tragically, even more die from complications. And, of course, we cannot dismiss the fact that animals, who are well recognized as having feelings and compassion, are killed for our consumption. In one year, the average American consumes 130 shellfish, forty fish, twenty-six chickens, one turkey, one-half of a pig, and one-tenth of a cow. This equates to 38,627 animals being slaughtered in the United States per minute, or tens of billions per year. The people who have the job of "processing" these animals develop an insensitivity to them, to the point of hitting, kicking, and stomping on them. If you are not fully aware of how animals are treated, I highly recommend that you watch a documentary on the subject, such as *Earthlings* or *Vegucated*.

Environmental Well-Being

Indigenous cultures view disease as an imbalance with our connection to the natural world that manifests in us in a variety of undesirable ways. Our increasingly unconscious separation from the planet underlies our unhealthy habits. If we were connected to the earth, we would not experience the poor health that we do. Nor would the earth suffer under our delusion that it can provide us with infinite resources.

As I came to realize that spirituality was at the core of my passion about nutrition, I wanted to strengthen that aspect of my understanding even further. So, while pregnant, I landed at Holy Names College in Oakland, California, to obtain a master's degree in culture and creation spirituality, under the guidance of Reverend Matthew Fox.

Creation spirituality encourages us to teach the story of the universe in such a way that we can identify ourselves within it and become part of its creative process. Because I was pregnant, and because the program centered on creativity, transformation, birth, and rebirth, I served as a living example of those concepts. During one of our class meditations, I had an image of being pregnant with the earth. In my vision, I was connected to the planet by a cosmological umbilical cord that both nourished the planet and removed waste from it. As I worked with this image, I considered that the human body is a microcosm of the earth, composed of the same elements in the same proportion: about three-quarters water and one-quarter solid, organic and inorganic. It was beautifully symbolic, given that the way

a woman eats during pregnancy has a significant impact on the health of her baby. Similar, but much less recognized, is the idea that the way each of us eats has a significant impact on the health of the planet.

This image of being pregnant with the earth then extended to a vision of every one of us being pregnant with the earth, just as we are all connected to the planet. Buddhist monk Thich Nhat Hanh says, "Even if you do not have a baby in your womb, the seed is already there. Even if you are not married, even if you are a man, you should be aware that a baby is already there, the seeds of future generations are already there." Placing the earth within our body helps remind us of our intimate connection with the natural world, our great dependence upon it for survival, and its great dependence upon us for survival.

In your mind's eye, imagine yourself being pregnant with the earth, connected by the cosmological umbilical cord I described, which both nourishes you and removes waste. See yourself picking an apple from a tree or a grape fresh from the vine—whatever is delicious to you. Bite into it, releasing its juices so you can taste its sweetness. As you chew and swallow, visualize your body digesting its individual nutrients. Some of those nutrients are then transported to the cells of your body so that you can perform your daily tasks or heal what needs to be healed. Others are transported through the umbilical cord to the planet that resides within you.

This may feel like a stretch—and pregnancy will do that to a person—but there is truth to this image of nurturing the womb: it reminds us of the fact that the human survives only within the larger complex of ecosystems. This is why a body-centered spirituality is necessary to bring about what has been called geo-justice. We cannot heal ourselves without healing the earth any more than we can heal the earth without healing ourselves. When it comes to our relationship with the earth, we can't have our cake and eat it, too; we cannot expect the earth to continue to provide for us if we continue to consume its natural resources.

Only by having a mutually supportive relationship with the earth do we have any chance of saving it from humankind's destruction. In 500 BC, the Greeks called the earth Gaía, an ancient term for the feminine personification of the "great mother of all." Today, the Gaía hypothesis is an ecological theory that states that all living and nonliving things make up a single organism. All of life must be sustained through the unity of its many parts. The earth cannot survive in fragments any more than the human body can. By necessity, a body-centered spirituality involves food. To that end, food provides us with a lifetime of opportunities to practice the compassion that eco-evolution requires. Ultimately, I want to support both us and our planet to function as authentically and optimally as possible. It's about expanded love, baby!

Clearly, making choices that benefit our individual health does not provide enough reason for many to do so, but perhaps the motivation to care for something greater than ourselves can. As I've noted, pregnant woman take better care of themselves during pregnancy than at any other time in their lives. They do this out of love and compassion for their unborn child, something they perceive to be of greater value than they are. Similarly, the image of being pregnant with the earth calls us to take better care of ourselves at *any* point in time, out of love and compassion for the earth, something also greater than we are. True and long-lasting incentive to do so must come from within, where compassion resides.

Ꮞ

You may be surprised to learn that the world has enough food to feed everyone. Global agriculture produces 17 percent more calories per person today than it did thirty years ago, despite a 70 percent population increase—enough to provide everyone in the world with at least 2,720 kilocalories (kcal) per person per day. The amount of vegetable protein used to grow cattle for our fast-food chains is equivalent to the world's protein deficiency. Meat production is tremendously energy intensive—it takes five to twenty calories of fossil fuel to produce one calorie of food energy in the form of meat—whereas it takes merely one-quarter to one-half of a calorie of fossil fuel to produce one calorie of plant energy food. Production of plant food is, therefore, ten to one hundred times more energy efficient than meat production.

The principal issue is that many people in the world do not have sufficient land to grow, or income to purchase, enough food. The Food and Agriculture Organization (FAO) published a report, "Livestock Long Shadow: Environmental Issues and Options," in 2006, placing blame on animal agriculture for all major environmental problems, including water scarcity and pollution, stating that "livestock detract more from total food supply than they provide." Production of meat and other animal products takes up over 90 percent of all agricultural land and uses nearly 80 percent of the consumption of water resources in the United States. Millions of acres of forestland in the United States are being lost each year to nonforest uses; two-thirds of those acres are sacrificed for cattle grazing. Australia has already lost 99 percent of its forests, in large part to

this purpose.

Perhaps most compelling is the impact of meat eating on global warming. Methane gas generated from factory livestock farming is responsible for more global warming than the emissions caused by cars and other forms of transportation. The FAO found that livestock production is responsible for 18 percent of humanity's greenhouse-gas emissions. Vast swaths of forest have been cleared for grazing (26 percent of all land worldwide) and growing livestock feed (33 percent of arable land). Livestock production contributes 37 percent of human-induced emissions of methane, which has a higher global-warming potential than carbon dioxide.

In addition, fertilizer, pesticide, herbicide, and livestock waste runoff severely pollutes our waterways. Animal excrement and fertilizers have been blamed for a large percentage of the nitrogen and phosphorus released into our rivers. Furthermore, the millions of tons of nonrecycled waste that livestock produce each year—which is substantially more concentrated than domestic raw sewage—generally ends up untreated in our water.

As the human population continues to grow, water needs will also become even more serious; the demand for global meat production is projected to more than double by 2050. Another FAO report warns that 64 percent of all people worldwide will live in water-stressed areas, compared with

38 percent today. "The production of animal protein requires 'significantly more' water than the production of plant protein because the quantity of water needed to grow the feedcrops and forage is substantial," point out ecologist Dr. David Pimentel and nutritionist Marcia Pimental, both of Cornell University, in their book, *Food, Energy, and Society*. The amount of water needed to make one McDonald's hamburger is roughly equal to the amount of water that a family of four in the Amazon uses in an entire month. That's because we need water to grow the plants that feed the cattle. From the perspective of sustainably feeding billions of people, feeding plants to animals and then feeding animals to humans will not work, at least not to the extent to which it is happening in 2014.

And what about our consumption of fish? According to an FAO estimate, over 70 percent of the world's fish species are either fully exploited or depleted. The choices we make as consumers drive the seafood marketplace. Overfishing threatens the diversity of marine life, depleting many fish ecosystems. In one year, the average American consumes 40 fish and 130 shellfish.

The magnitude of this issue hit me while on a family vacation on Maui. We went to eat at a local restaurant, and, of course, the majority of the menu items included fish. It struck me that just about everyone in that restaurant would be eating fish during his or her meal, and that this must be going on in hundreds of restaurants on the island and in thousands of restaurants across the country all day long. There simply aren't enough fish in the ocean to support that level of consumption for much longer.

In his book, *Oceana: Our Endangered Oceans and What We Can Do to Save Them*, Ted Danson reports that humans have depleted over 90 percent of the ocean's top predators—sharks, bluefin tuna, swordfish, marlin, and king mackerel—in just fifty-five years. According to Greenpeace, the depletion of these top predators can shift entire oceanic ecosystems to the point where, in this century, we may see bumper crops of jellyfish replacing the fish consumed by humans.

And then there are the nontargeted animals—like turtles, dolphins, and sea birds—that are caught along with these top predators. Called by-catch, these animals are usually thrown back into the ocean dead or dying. Farm fishing is an attempt to compensate for the lack of fish in the ocean. But, as Danson states, "Aquaculture, or farm fishing, requires feed for captive fish. To grow just one pound of farmed salmon, an estimated four to eleven pounds of prey fish are consumed. As the aquaculture industry continues to expand, prey fish are depleted at alarming and unsustainable rates. If current trends continue, some researchers predict that aquaculture will outgrow the supply of fishmeal as soon as 2020." And *National Geographic* reports that "a study of catch data published in 2006 in the journal *Science* grimly predicted that if fishing rates continue apace, *all* the world's fisheries will have collapsed by the year 2048."

࿔

Whether we are addressing our food-related health crisis from an individual, communal, or environmental standpoint, we need to dig deep to get to the root of the problem. We must awaken to the fact that we are one with ourselves and one with each other, and that we have unconsciously pushed ourselves into a global food frenzy. Heavier than ever, we spend billions of dollars on weight-loss programs and products while billions of other people hunger for food every day. And, as a joint analysis released by the Center on Hunger & Poverty at Brandeis University and the Food Research and Action Center shows, hunger and obesity not only pose separate and distinct health risks but also can coexist in the same household. Clearly, external hunger cues, along with the food industry's influence in altering our foods, have disturbed our natural state of equilibrium. This unnatural state is reflected by the suffering health of the earth.

I believe that the individual, communal, and environmental conditions that I have described above are in desperate need of our response. As the November 2014 McKinsey Global Obesity Report states, education and personal responsibility are critical elements of any program aiming to reduce obesity, but they are not sufficient on their own. Rather, we need a variety of sustainable strategies to reverse our health conditions, starting with redefining environmental and societal norms, such as reducing portion sizes, changing marketing practices, and restructuring urban and education environments to facilitate physical activities. Healing our health crisis requires engagement from as many sectors as possible—governments, retailers, consumer-goods companies, restaurants, employers, media organizations, educators, and health care providers. But let us not forget that those sectors are made up of individuals, and, as such, we have the opportunity to make a difference now.

In Stan Lee's *Spider-Man*, Uncle Ben advised Peter Parker, "With great power comes great responsibility." Indeed, each one of us has much more power than we realize in regard to how we eat. In taking *responsibility* for our health, we have the *ability to respond* to our current health crisis. We have the power—which lies in the free will we exercise every time we make a choice about how and what to eat—to make this a world that supports us, each other, and the planet.

CHAPTER FIVE

What is the Earth Serving Up?

WE LIVE IN human bodies on a planet that provides everything we need to sustain them. When it comes to nourishing the human body, it makes sense to look first at what the earth serves up for us to eat. I mean this in the literal sense. That is, in addition to water, which covers a majority of the planet, what actually grows from the ground that is intended for our consumption? Fruits, vegetables, grains, legumes, nuts, and seeds all grow from the earth—under and in dirt, and on bushes, vines, and trees. In this chapter, I will provide an overview of each of these types of plants, including a description of their history and sacred symbolism. Life that swims in the oceans (fish) and walks on the land (animals) will be discussed in the following two chapters.

Water

Water is the most abundant substance on Earth, as well as in the human body. In fact, 70 percent of the earth is covered with water and 70 percent of the body is made up of water. Water has also captivated human interest as an instructive element: Spiritual teachers around the world associate water with wisdom. Water is mentioned 436 times in the Bible. In ancient Greece, water gods, such as Oceanus and Pontus, often symbolized qualities of intelligence, because knowledge was associated with the immensity and depths of the ocean and seas. And the Chinese incorporate water into the philosophy and practice of feng shui, the art of creating harmonious and balanced surroundings.

Constantly moving from one place to another and from one form to another, water also serves as a remarkable symbol of transformation. Consider that just two molecules, hydrogen and oxygen, can restructure themselves over and over into different states: liquid, vapor, and solid. And, as with oxygen, we cannot live without it—it is essential to almost every physiological reaction in the body. As such, it is imperative that you drink water regularly if you want to give your body the best chance possible to experience optimal health.

Given how many people want to transform their bodies by losing weight, it makes sense to begin by developing a habit of drinking clean water. Drinking water between meals helps fill the stomach so that you are not as likely to overeat. It also helps the gastrointestinal tract adapt to a high-fiber diet and proper cell function, both of which are essential

for weight loss. Drink at least half your body weight in ounces to facilitate optimal health, as well as healthy, glowing skin and a high level of energy.

Tips for Drinking Enough Water Each Day

- Take a water break instead of a coffee break. Try warm water with a slice of fresh lemon.
- Keep a reusable cup or bottle of water handy. Some schools provide students with a water bottle to keep at their school desks. This alone serves as a reminder to drink more water.
- Keep a bottle of water in your backpack or purse.
- Drink a cup of water after you go to the restroom.
- Eat lots and lots of foods with high water content, like soup, and especially fruits and vegetables.
- When someone offers you a glass of water, say yes.

For some, sipping water throughout the day works well. For others, drinking water a glass at a time is the easiest way to ensure an adequate intake. Find a method that works for you, and grow conscious about following it.

How do you know if you are drinking enough? While it has become generally recommended that we drink half our body weight in ounces, this approach does not account for differences in people's lifestyle and eating habits. For example, someone who does, indeed, consume a lot of fruits and vegetables is not going to need to drink as much water because those foods contain a high percentage of water which is contributed to the body. The best approach is to listen to your body—there is a reason we have a thirst mechanism—and to use your head. When you feel thirsty, drink water, not '-ades,' 'punches,' or 'energy drinks.' And, at the same time, keep in mind that if you are spending a lot of time out in the sun or engaging in physical exercise causing you to sweat, you will need to drink more water than usual. Further, keep in mind that while many foods and beverages contain water and therefore add to one's fluid intake, the caffeine in coffee, tea, and other caffeinated beverages has a diuretic effect that increases water loss through urination. The more caffeine you consume, the greater the potential for increased water loss. Another clue is to check the color of your urine. Dark yellow urine is a sign that you are not drinking enough water, so drink up until your output is clear.

Because of the pollutants that become a part of our water supply, choosing a type of water to drink has become an issue. First and foremost, it is not necessary or recommended that you drink so-called "vitamin waters." As we will discuss in further detail, adding isolated nutrients to food is generally not advised, nor, contrary to popular belief, is drinking fluoridated water, since some have suggested that it can lead to calcification of the pineal gland, part of our nervous system considered as the gateway to consciousness. We will discuss this subject in more detail in chapter 10. Of course, drinking any water is probably better than not drinking water at all, but for highest quality, I suggest that you drink distilled water, spring water, or water that has undergone reverse osmosis.

Plants, Plants, and More Plants

While water is absolutely necessary for human life, it is not enough, because while water is essential to creating energy, it does not provide it. We must consume food in order to get energy to stay alive and perform our activities. Energy comes in three forms—carbohydrate, protein, and fat—which our body converts into calories. Plants provide all of these types of energy, as well as thousands and thousands of vitamins, minerals, and phytonutrients—plant compounds, like antioxidants, that aid in disease prevention and health maintenance. Again, in this section, we are focusing on food that grows from the ground: fruit, vegetables, grains, legumes, nuts, seeds, herbs, and spices. I will refer just briefly to some of the key attributes that make these different types of plants so amazing at both nourishing and, when necessary, healing the body. A more detailed explanation of the nutritional attributes of plants appears in chapter 7.

Fruit

Feminine fruit is Mother Nature's crown jewel. All fruits develop from a plant's flower and are the matured part of the plant's ovary. Sweet! And while all fruits share this commonality, they are wonderfully varied in appearance and taste. Consider, for example, a pineapple as compared with a banana as compared with a watermelon. There are actually several subcategories of fruit, such as pomes (apples and pears), drupes (apricots, peaches, nectarines, and plums), berries (raspberries, cranberries, blueberries, blackberries, elderberries, and so on), citrus fruits (oranges, mandarins, grapefruit, lemons, and limes), and melons (watermelons, cantaloupe, honeydew, casaba, and so on). What about bananas and papayas? Botanically, they are similar to berries but seem to be in a class of their own. And while the majority of fruits are oh so sweet, there are some outliers—like tomatoes and peppers—that we commonly refer to as vegetables. Maybe this is Mother Nature's way of reminding us not to judge a book by its cover.

Highly symbolic, fruit appears in myths and religious ritual and teachings throughout the world. In general, it often represents abundance, or "fruitfulness."

Apples, cherries, coconuts, figs, pears, plums, pomegranate, and strawberries, for example, all carry special meaning within different traditions.

Let's consider an apple. In Celtic paganism, the Goddess's apple signified a sacred marriage. Apple blossoms were wedding flowers because they represented the virgin form of the Goddess, whose maturity produced the fruit. In China, apple blossoms signify feminine beauty, and the fruit itself represents peace. Further, it was customary for a gypsy girl to choose her lover by tossing him an apple, which served as a sexual symbol. Fruit also signifies gluttony and temptation. Most are familiar with the

Old Testament story of Adam and Eve, who received awareness by biting into an apple from the forbidden tree, thereby casting themselves from paradise. Apples also offer hope of healing and immortality in Greek and Celtic mythology; today, we say simply, "An apple a day keeps the doctor away."

Fruits are good sources of fiber, both soluble and insoluble, which is one of the reasons they are the cornerstone of most detoxification diets. Sugar has justifiably gotten a bad rap in recent decades, but the

sugars in fruit are not to blame. There is nothing more natural or more necessary to human health than the sugar that fruit naturally provides. It is the fuel that the brain wants most!

Fruits contain a combination of sugars, called fructose, glucose, and sucrose. Sucrose is the primary of these sugars, though fructose is the sweetest. The sugar in fruit, in combination with its high water content—80–95 percent—makes it an ideal snack for weight loss and otherwise. In countries like Italy, fruit often serves as dessert. Fruits also provide minerals—such as potassium (bananas, pears, oranges) and iron (berries and dried fruits), calcium, and magnesium—and are an excellent source of vitamins, particularly vitamin C and beta-carotene, the precursor of vitamin A.

Minimally, two servings of fruit are recommended each day. A serving is one medium fresh fruit, one-half cup cooked or cut-up fruit, one-half cup 100 percent fruit juice, or one-quarter cup dried fruit.

Vegetables

Vegetables offer the greatest diversity among plants. People who claim that they don't like vegetables probably aren't aware that there are hundreds of varieties, which comprise a rainbow of colors—including red, orange, yellow, green, purple, and white—as well as an impressive range of flavor and texture. Vegetables are classified as leafy greens (spinach, salad greens, collards, kale, radicchio, and watercress); flowers, buds, and stalks (celery, broccoli, cauliflower, asparagus, and artichokes); seeds and pods (snap beans, lima beans, peas, and sweet corn); roots, bulbs, and tubers (onions, turnips, potatoes, beets, carrots, radishes, and parsnips); and fruit vegetables (eggplants, squashes, peppers, and tomatoes). And let's not forget the exotic varieties, such as atemoya, carambola, cactus pear, cherimoya, lychee, and Ugli fruit, to name just a few. Most vegetables can be eaten raw or cooked and can be frozen or canned. They can be served up by themselves as a snack or used as an ingredient in sauces, soups, casseroles, and dishes as extensive as the creative chef can imagine.

Symbolically, vegetables are similar to fruit. In ancient Egypt, for example, the onion symbolized eternity because of its concentric circular structure. Paintings of onions appear on the inner walls of both pyramids and tombs. And, for the same reason, Russian and other orthodox churches are designed with bulb-shaped domes having a pointy top. In China, the onion represents cleverness.

Vegetables also take center stage when it comes to providing the most nutrition per calorie; kale, collard greens, spinach, and turnip greens take the lead in this regard. Veggies contain thousands of phytonutrients (plant nutrients), including a wide array of antioxidants and vitamins, such as vitamin C, vitamin K, and beta-carotene (which the body converts to vitamin A), and minerals, such as potassium, iron, folate, and calcium. Cruciferous vegetables, like cabbage, broccoli, bok choy, brussels sprouts, kale, and cauliflower, have been shown to lower risk for heart disease and cancer, perhaps through their ability to reduce inflammation. Minimally, five servings of vegetables per day are recommended. A serving size is one-half cup cooked vegetable, one cup raw vegetable, or one-half cup vegetable juice. The most recent recommendation from the US Department of Agriculture is to eat at least seven to thirteen or more servings of fruits *and* vegetables per day. Visually, the idea is to fill half your plate with fruits and vegetables—thus, about one-quarter of your plate with fruits. I like to adhere to the slogan "fruits and veggies: more matters," which reminds us that when it comes to optimal health, there is no upper limit to the amount of fruits and vegetables we can consume.

Grains

When was the last time you picked spaghetti from the ground? How about a loaf of bread or a tortilla? While we think of these foods as grains, they are actually processed foods made from grains that grow from the earth. So let's ask, once again, what grains *does* the earth serve up?

Amaranth, for example, made its appearance eight thousand years ago as an ancient grain with Aztec roots. According to *The UC Berkeley Wellness*

Encyclopedia of Food and Nutrition, "Cortes, the Spanish conqueror of the Aztecs, outlawed the cultivation of amaranth, effectively starving the Aztecs into submission and destroying their culture. As a direct result of the conquistador's decree, knowledge of amaranth was virtually lost to the Western world for hundreds of years. Sometime after the fifteenth century, however, amaranth was brought to Asia, where it found favor on the Indian subcontinent and in China, which is the largest producer of the grain today." It was offered as a royal tribute and used in religious rituals. Other ancient grains include quinoa and millet. Because grains are so closely tied to the act of harvesting, they often symbolize success, prosperity, material wealth, and payment for work. The harvest often represents the truth because it provides evidence of what has grown. Biblical references compare straw with wheat, for example, making the point that the word of a false prophet or that of a foolish dreamer is not as sound as God's word.

From couscous in North Africa to rice in China, grains are the primary form of sustenance, providing about half of the world's calories, throughout the world. Others include barley, brown and wild rice, buckwheat, bulgur, rye, sorghum, spelt, and triticale. And then there are the grains most familiar to our Western society: wheat, corn, and oats (half of which animals eat and then we eventually consume through their products, like meat, milk, cheese, and eggs).

Contrary to popular belief, whole grains are actually quite easy and fast to prepare; they're even terrific travel companions on backpacking and camping trips. Between 65 and 90 percent of the calories in whole grains come from carbohydrates (mostly complex), thereby providing four calories per gram and both soluble and insoluble fiber. These factors make them beneficial to weight loss, despite their unfortunate bad rap as being fattening. Amaranth is making a comeback in Western culture due to its near-miraculous nutrition content. That is, amaranth, unlike most grains, contains high-quality protein in the form of the amino acid lysine. It is also especially high in iron, providing four times as much as that in brown rice and twice as much as that in bulgur. Today, it is mostly available in health-food stores, online, or in whole-food products like JuicePlus+ Complete. Grains provide significant amounts of B vitamins (riboflavin, thiamin, and niacin), vitamin E, iron, zinc, calcium, selenium, and magnesium. At least five servings of grains, preferably whole grains, are recommended per day. A serving is one-half cup cooked cereal, pasta, rice, or other grain; one ounce ready-to-eat cereal; one slice bread or one six-inch tortilla; or one-half cup white or sweet potato or corn.

Legumes

Dried beans, peas, and lentils are collectively called legumes. Beans include adzuki beans, black beans, cannellini beans, cranberry beans, fava beans, flageolets, garbanzo beans, great northern beans, kidney beans, lima beans, mung beans, navy beans, pinto beans, small red beans, and soybeans. Dried peas include black-eyed peas, chickpeas, and split peas (yellow and green). Lentils include brown, green, and red varieties. Botanically, peanuts, while commonly considered a nut, are also in this category. Although they all belong to a single plant, they come in various forms: in pods (soybeans), on climbing vines (lima beans), and on trees (carob beans). Inexpensive and versatile, legumes are eaten both fresh and dried and are prized staple foods throughout the world, from adzuki beans in China to black beans in Latin America to chickpeas in the Middle East.

Legumes date back about ten thousand years, having been found in Egyptian tombs and frequently referred to in the Bible. Whereas grains deplete nitrogen in the soil, legumes produce it and are thus especially valuable to crop rotation in agriculture. Symbolically, because they expand or swell when cooked, peas represent prosperity. Black-eyed peas, especially, are thought to bring good luck. They have traditionally been eaten at Rosh Hashanah, the Jewish new year, as recorded in the Babylonian Talmud, and on January 1 in the southern United States, in order to bring prosperity into the new year. Similarly, red beans are eaten at special ceremonies in Asian cultures because of their color, which is generally thought to bring good fortune.

Legumes are low in fat and are the richest source of protein among plant foods, providing about eight grams of protein per serving. They also are a good source of lysine, the essential amino acid that is low in most grains. Soy and foods made from soybeans, such as tofu, soymilk, tempeh, and veggie meats, provide even more protein. While controversial, my extensive review of research on soy concludes that it is beneficial to health. The only caveat is that you must purchase organic soy and soy products, since soy is a crop that tends to be genetically modified. High in soluble fiber, beans are digested slowly and are thus a tremendous help to diabetics, who when they regularly consume a substantial amount of beans require less insulin to control their blood sugar. Beans also provide minerals, like iron and zinc.

Three to four daily servings of legumes are recommended. A serving is one-half cup cooked beans, tofu, or tempeh; one ounce "veggie meat"; one cup fortified soy milk or three-quarters of a cup of fortified soy yogurt; or two tablespoons peanut butter, one-quarter cup peanuts, or one-quarter cup soy nuts.

Nuts

The earth provides a wide variety of nuts—which are dry, single-seeded fruits enclosed in a tough outer layer—that grow all over the world in assorted shapes, sizes, textures, and flavors. These

include almonds, Brazil nuts, cashew nuts, chestnuts, coconuts, filberts, hazelnuts, macadamia nuts, pecans, pine nuts, pistachio nuts, and walnuts. Nuts have been an important source of nutrition throughout human history. Nomadic peoples gathered them growing in the wild, and around 10,000 BC, settled populations began to cultivate nut trees. Native Americans taught the European colonists to prepare nuts to turn into pastes, flours, oils, and liquids.

Nuts' hard outer shells have made them a long-standing symbol of toughness. Consider the familiar saying "That's a tough nut to crack." They can also represent perseverance and an ability to withstand hardship. I will never forget the time my sons tried to break open a coconut. They worked for hours to open up that shell. Eventually, they asked a local Costa Rican for advice. He took the coconut in his hands and threw it onto the ground. Done!

Once the nut is cracked, its symbolic value

extends to its contents. For example, if the inside is tender and flavorful, one's efforts are expected to be fruitful. If the inside is rotten or bitter, plans may not come to fruition. This is the meaning behind the tradition of giving sugared almonds as favors at baby showers and weddings, a tradition that originated with the ancient Romans. Jewish tradition refers to the nut for symbolic application for many reasons. Among them, nuts symbolize the scholar, because just as the kernel remains untouched when a nut falls to the ground, so does the Torah stay clean even when its student sins. Also, the roots of a nut tree, unlike those of other trees, will revive after exposure, even though they may have begun to wither; similarly, Jews are forgiven if they confess, or expose, their sins.

Nuts are very high in calories, about 80 percent of which come from fat. Most have 160 to 190 calories and fourteen to nineteen grams of fat per ounce. Besides being a good source of many nutrients, including protein, fiber, vitamins (B vitamins and vitamin E), minerals (magnesium, zinc, copper, and selenium), and polyphenolic antioxidants (resveratrol), the fat in nuts, particularly walnuts and almonds, is primarily unsaturated—monounsaturated and polyunsaturated—and reduces the risk of chronic disease, particularly heart disease. Nuts have also been shown to support brain function. Further, partly because of their high fat content, nuts also have a high satiety value.

Despite concern that nuts' high fat content may promote weight gain, no deleterious effects on body weight have been observed in either epidemiological or clinical trials. It seems that nuts' bioavailability limits the body's absorption of the energy, or calories, they contain. One to two servings of nuts is recommended every day. A serving is two tablespoons of a nut butter or one-quarter cup of nuts.

Seeds

Seeds are the very genesis of the life force in our food system. Seeds are a flowering plant's unit of reproduction. Provided water, sunlight, and nutrients, seeds develop into other such plants, continuing life from one generation to the next, both for themselves and for humans. While we generally think of seeds for planting, many seeds are edible—including chia seeds, flax seeds, hemp seeds, pumpkin seeds, rapeseeds, sesame seeds, and sunflower seeds—and others are used as spices, such as caraway, coriander, dill, and fennel.

Seeds also play an important part in many traditions around the world. Consider the popular custom of carving pumpkins into jack-o'-lanterns and then toasting the seeds. Some seeds, like sunflower seeds, can be eaten in their shell and are therefore a popular snack at baseball games, or can be removed from it so they're easier to use in food preparation and less challenging to snack on. And most can be used to make pastes, butters, milks, and oils or incorporated into salads, soups, candy, and an endless array of other dishes.

Highly symbolic, seeds represent such ideas as potential, hope, initiation, reproduction, fruitfulness, and provision. It is not uncommon to hear, for example, that someone has "planted the seeds" of some desired outcome, whether it be a new crop, a dream home, or something else. The seed reminds us that what once seemed lifeless can bring new life. Many are familiar with the parable of the mustard seed:

> **31** *He told them another parable: "The kingdom of heaven is like a mustard seed, which a man took and planted in his field.* **32** *Though it is the smallest of all seeds, yet when it grows, it is the largest of garden plants and becomes a tree, so that the birds come and perch in its branches."*
>
> (*Matthew 13:31–32*).

We cannot easily see the process that leads a dry seed to become a tree that moves with the wind. We must trust that the potential of our idea will indeed bloom and grow.

Diverse in size—consider a sesame seed compared with a coconut—seeds pack in the nutrition! Indeed, ounce for ounce, seeds, like nuts, are high in calories but also rich in healthy polyunsaturated and monounsaturated fats, vitamins, minerals, and phytonutrients. Seeds are a good source of fiber, even more than nuts, especially when eaten with their shells or hulls. They also contain phytochemicals, some of which may have cardio-protective or anticancer effects. Some seeds, such as sunflower seeds, are among the best sources of vitamin E. Flaxseeds are rich in alpha-linolenic aid, a fat similar to the omega-3s in fish. Rapeseeds, from which canola oil is made, also contain alpha-linolenic acid, as do hemp seeds. Sunflower, pumpkin, squash, and sesame seeds supply iron, potassium, and phosphorus as well. One to two servings of seeds are recommended every day. A serving is two tablespoons of a seed butter or whole seeds.

Herbs and Spices

Herbs and spices are Mother Nature's secret ingredients! Plants whose leaves or seeds are used as food, they mostly add flavor, but also color and preservation, to food. In addition, herbs and spices have been used to preserve the dead, as gifts and tribute to nobility, to establish trade routes between countries, as perfumes and dyes, and for medicinal purposes. There are far too many to mention here, but more familiar varieties include allspice, anise, basil, bay leaf, cardamom, cayenne, cilantro, cinnamon, cloves, ginger, mace, mint, nutmeg, oregano, paprika, parsley, pepper, rosemary, saffron, sage, tarragon, thyme, and turmeric.

Most of us are familiar with the term "the spice of life." Indeed, herbs and spices can turn the blandest food into something unforgettable. My son Eric backpacked through Death Valley for twenty-eight days in the spring of 2014, as a junior in high school. The food on that trip included dehydrated vegetable soups and mashed potatoes; pasta, couscous, quinoa, and brown rice; and lots and lots of spices. Eric and one of the other "ringtails" were responsible for resupplying the group's spice kit with curry powder, Italian seasonings, salt, pepper, red pepper flakes, garlic powder, cinnamon, and hot sauce (Tapatío and sriracha). The spices almost magically turned dehydrated mashed potatoes into something awesome. "From now on, I'm gonna want a spice kit available," Eric said upon his return.

Each herb and spice carries its own significance. For example, bay represents glory. (Imagine the bay-leaf crowns the ancient Romans wore.) The rich variety of herbs and spices in the Near East resulted in the Bible's thousands of references to them, including the account of the three wise men who brought frankincense and myrrh, both aromatic herbs, to the newborn king.

A raving fan of the symbolic world, I like to encourage people to discover the spices that have been hidden or forgotten in the dark corners of their cupboard during the dark winter months. For, though we cannot see it, life abounds in the dark. Consider that the first nine months of human life are spent in the absolute darkness of a mother's womb; or that the gift you have received from a dear friend cannot be seen until the package is opened; or that many vegetables grow underground in dark, cold, rich soil. As you reach into your cupboard for those hidden and forgotten spices, reflect upon those lost, hidden, suppressed, and denied aspects of yourself that are waiting to be held with love and compassion. By embracing these aspects, you can bring them more fully into the light. After all, who can see the stars unless it's dark?

Herbs and spices make it easy for people to enjoy rich flavor without having to add a lot of fat or calories to food. Because they're low in sodium, they can be an ideal substitute for salt. And while many people are just beginning to recognize them for their medicinal qualities, including antimicrobial and antioxidant activity, herbs and spices are indeed nature's botanical pharmacy. In fact, the vast majority of prescription and over-the-counter medications used today are based on the reactions of various herbs and spices in the human body.

When obtaining my degree in spirituality, I learned that an in-depth understanding of food and nutrition were central to being recognized as a shaman, or native healer. That is quite simply because plants, with their high concentrations of nutrient compounds, provide the most effective healing properties. To name just a few examples: aloe helps heal burns, ginger lessens nausea and vomiting in pregnant women, and cinnamon improves blood sugar levels in diabetics. Since herbs and spices contain virtually no calories or sodium, you may enjoy them to your heart's content!

We will address the nutritional benefits of plant foods in even greater detail in chapter 6. But while research is always beneficial, even necessary, to understanding the impact of various foods, it is common sense that drives the Sacred Art of Eating. And when you follow common sense, good things happen.

Imperfectly Vegan

Nothing will benefit human health and increase chances for survival of life on Earth as much as the evolution to a vegetarian diet.

—Albert Einstein

VEGETARIAN NUTRITION began in the sixth century BC with the famous Greek philosopher and mathematician Pythagoras. Among other things, he was considered the father of ethical vegetarianism. He influenced many of his peers, including Plato. However, after the fall of ancient Greece, vegetarian nutrition practically disappeared in Europe until the Renaissance era, when the genius Leonardo da Vinci revitalized the idea. During the Age of Enlightenment, outstanding personalities like Rousseau, Voltaire, and Wesley practiced vegetarian nutrition. Today, it represents an increasingly popular diet with an international following.

People choose to embrace a vegetarian lifestyle for various reasons, including religious, health-based, environmental, and social. Those reasons tend to change with experience. For example, someone who adopts a vegetarian lifestyle may do so for health reasons. But as that person learns more about this new way of eating, and as his or her health improves as a result of successful attempts at it, his or her primary motivation may become a desire to support the environment or not to participate in cruelty to animals. As consciousness grows, so does the number of people turning toward a vegetarian and vegan lifestyle. A 2009 study from the CDC found that about one in two hundred young Americans, or 367,000 US children, are vegetarians.

Generally, there are four different types of vegetarian diets:

- Vegan: a vegetarian diet that excludes all animal products, such as meat, poultry, fish, eggs, milk, cheese, and other dairy products.

- Lacto-vegetarian: a vegetarian diet that excludes meat, poultry, fish, and eggs but includes dairy products.

- Lacto-ovo-vegetarian: a vegetarian diet that excludes meat, poultry, and fish but includes eggs and dairy products. Most vegetarians in the United States fall into this category.

- Semivegetarian or flexitarian: a semivegetarian diet with a focus on vegetarian food, but involving occasional consumption of meat, poultry, or fish.

And now, introducing a new type of vegetarian lifestyle: Imperfectly Vegan™. I created this term for the following reasons:

- A vegan diet is healthiest for both humans and the earth.

- A traditional vegan diet is too extreme for most people to want to attempt.

- Even some of the most committed vegans will deviate, whether consciously or not.

- Vegetarianism can be vague, but using a term that includes the word "vegan" keeps the focus on a plant-based diet.

- Following a vegan diet *most* of the time is realistic and provides huge benefits to health, to animals, and to the planet.

- Being Imperfectly Vegan is a spiritual path toward increased consciousness and unity of body, mind, and spirit.

- Being Imperfectly Vegan is nutritious and delicious!

I first came up with this term in response to people asking me about my lifestyle: "Are you a vegetarian?" Well, not exactly. And then I'd have to explain in which ways I was or wasn't a vegetarian. "Are you a vegan?" That felt close, but I never felt comfortable calling myself a vegan, because there are times when I do consume animal products, both consciously and not. And so I began to respond by saying that I am Imperfectly Vegan. I noticed that people seemed to understand what I meant without my having to explain anything. At more than one event when I have unveiled this term, I have even heard a collective sigh in the room.

Imperfectly Vegan piques people's curiosity, and many seem interested in locating themselves within that definition. It feels doable and represents a clearer step toward plant-based eating than vegetarianism does; it engenders a sense of peace, ease, and hope in people who are interested in following a vegetarian diet but are unsure whether they can successfully do so; and it seems to make sense to those who already practice a vegan lifestyle but admit to consuming small amounts of animal foods from time to time.

Being Imperfectly Vegan is about making a commitment to all of life. It also allows for a dose of reality. Certainly, increasing numbers of animal rights activists, environmentalists, and health professionals are working toward a vegan world and are thus steadfast in their commitment to a vegan lifestyle. The degree to which someone is Imperfectly Vegan depends on his or her personal level of commitment, experience, and circumstances, all of which may change at different points in time. While the health advantages of a vegetarian diet compared with those of a nonvegetarian diet are well documented and highly significant, when it comes to giving up eggs and small amounts of dairy, those differences are not as significant. As such, the reason for abstaining from these foods rests on the cruelty that is inflicted upon the animals providing them and concerns for the environment.

In the field of nutrition, we speak of dietary patterns. There is an important distinction between assessing a person's nutrient intake based on an overall pattern of eating versus just one meal or even a full day of eating. In regard to being Imperfectly Vegan, this means that it is much more beneficial that someone strive to eat a plant-based diet most of the time, with an occasional turn to animal foods, than to eat an omnivorous diet most of the time, with the occasional absence of flesh. Not to allow

for the small inclusion of animal foods would mean that fewer people would attempt a plant-based diet at all. Would I love to see everyone follow a plant-based diet? Absolutely! But my training and education in public health have made me all too aware of the realities behind such a desire. Thus, offering up the practice of being Imperfectly Vegan provides an avenue that more and more people can practice without undue pressure to be absolutist or extremist. And, as your experience with a plant-based diet grows, you will find that animal products are increasingly less appetizing and satisfying for various reasons.

Throwing out a new term may mess with the heads of reputable nutrition researchers, but it would be a very good problem to have! Many have already joined me in being Imperfectly Vegan, and some were willing to describe their experience to me for this book.

My friend StaciJoy Ellis, a holistic nurse, says, "'Imperfectly Vegan' is a very powerful term to me because it describes how I eat in a way that gives me self-compassion for when I am not perfectly vegan. So when I have a bit of goat cheese on my salad or a bite of a quiche, I still feel that I am being congruent with my description of being Imperfectly Vegan."

Another friend, Sean Butman, who has more recently adopted a plant-based diet, says, "Imperfectly Vegan, for me, is a mindset that I will

I also read a story about a twentysomething guy, G. E. Miller, who wrote about how he and his wife gradually moved toward a plant-based diet. He says, "Today, I very occasionally eat poultry, seafood, and if in an 'eat it or miss a meal' situation, I'll still eat just about anything. For the most part though, I'd classify myself as a non-strict vegetarian." I'd say he's Imperfectly Vegan!

The Health Benefits of Being Imperfectly Vegan

Because vegans comprise a small percentage of the population, it is challenging to conclude much about their disease rates. Yet, despite the complexity and challenges involved in attaining evidence that confirms the health advantages of vegetarian nutrition, the benefits are well documented. Vegetarian categories combined have a significantly lower mortality rate than nonvegetarian ones. In other words, their practitioners live longer. As a reminder, heart disease and cancer are the two leading causes of death, but both of them are preventable. One of the primary reasons a plant-based lifestyle is so effective at reducing the risk of these diseases is that it helps people maintain a healthy weight. Lower body weight is associated with reduced mortality (death) and morbidity (illness) across the life span.

not become dogmatic in my approach to being vegan. Although I'm vegan for moral and ethical, as well as health, reasons, it's my own path to walk, and if I mistakenly have something that has cheese or milk or honey in it, I won't berate myself for it and I won't chastise the sources of that food, and instead will still thank them for their efforts. It means knowing the difference between having compassion for all life on this planet, regardless of what that life looks like or which animal or plant kingdom we've placed it into. Imperfectly Vegan also helps me avoid using vegan philosophy to pretend I'm better than those who aren't vegan."

Spiritual teacher Phil Isaia says, "Imperfectly Vegan resonates with me. Nobody's perfect, after all. And it's not oppressive. It takes the pressure off!"

Consistent evidence from clinical trials shows that vegetarian (especially vegan) diets reduce body weight. Population-based studies have shown that body weight, or body mass index (BMI), is lower for vegetarians than for nonvegetarians, and that the caloric intake of a vegetarian diet can be as many as 460 calories lower than that of nonvegetarians. It's hard to eat too much when you're focused on plant foods!

If you are overweight, even modest weight loss can help you improve cholesterol levels, reduce triglyceride levels, lower blood pressure, lower blood glucose (sugar) levels, and significantly reduce your risk of developing diabetes, all of which are risk factors for heart disease. In regard to cancer, researchers report that as many as ninety thousand

cancer deaths could be prevented each year if Americans maintained a healthy weight.

Further, a plant-based diet can reduce our risk of all cancers combined, especially gastrointestinal cancer, cancer of the female organs (including breast, ovarian, uterine, and cervical), and possibly respiratory cancer, because of the highly beneficial compounds found in plants. Evidence suggests, for example, that dietary phytochemicals, such as genistein, and other isoflavones from soy products; epigallocatechin-3-gallate and other polyphenols in tea; and isothiocyanates and indole-3-carbinol from cruciferous vegetables are likely to alter a person's susceptibility to cancer. Being Imperfectly Vegan is a sound strategy for losing weight, keeping it off for good, and enjoying the health benefits! In addition to living longer, vegetarians also age more healthfully—with advantages such as better age-related cognitive (brain) function, reduced cataracts, and reduced diverticular disease—and experience physical benefits like healthy, glowing skin and increased energy.

Needless to say, prevention is the way to go. Unfortunately, the medical system focuses money and energy on symptoms, rather than cause. So, for instance, if a woman removes her breast because she has breast cancer, that does not ensure that she will not get cancer again. If the underlying cause is not attended to, other cells are likely to experience the same fate. When it comes to chronic disease, medical intervention is often a shortsighted approach that harms more than it heals. The unhealthy cells underlying our diseases are constantly transforming. Provided with an optimal plant-based diet, they may regenerate, recover, and become revitalized.

While working toward my degree in nutrition and clinical dietetics at UC Berkeley, I was diagnosed with cervical cancer and was told that I would have to have surgery. Having a strong understanding of the power of whole foods to heal the human body, I said, "Well, Doc, do you think I could work on that myself for a while first?" (That was back in the days when I did a lot of "asking for permission.") In any case, that's what I did: I prayed, I visualized, and I ate lots and lots of raw carrots. When I went back to the doctor, to his surprise and my delight, it was gone! About twenty years later, the same situation occurred, except that this time I didn't *ask* the doctor if I could work on it myself; I *told* him that I was going to do that. Though it took a bit longer, I experienced a full recovery.

Of course, everyone's situation is unique and should be handled with his or her health care professionals accordingly. Many have cautioned me about suggesting that diet can cure cancer or other diseases, in the way way I was cautioned not to give the impression that one can overcome OCD through sincere surrender. I agree that each individual situation must be assessed, and, of course, much depends upon the advancement of one's condition, but I also know that in both cases, my healing resulted from using tools (food and a change of mind) that are available to each and every one of us. As Hippocrates said, "Let food be thy medicine."

Remember that "disease" is just a word that is used to refer to unhealthy cells in the body. The same issues underlie most diseases. So, in addition to helping to prevent or reverse heart disease and cancer, a plant-based diet may also facilitate the healing of most most conditions. Though having varied degrees of research, these include asthma, allergies, and sinus infections; skin disorders, such as acne; endometriosis and infertility; migraines; depression and other psychological disorders; heartburn; arthritis; joint pain; attention deficit disorder (ADD) and attention deficit hyperactivity disorder (ADHD); thyroid dysfunction; Lyme disease; chronic fatigue syndrome; autoimmune disorders, such as fibromyalgia and lupus; leaky-gut syndrome; and gastrointestinal disorders, such as Crohn's disease, irritable bowel syndrome (IBS), celiac disease, diverticulitis, and ulcerative colitis.

The body is wise beyond our understanding. In our cocreative relationship, it is our job to feed it well so that it can best do its job in helping us to live a full and healthy life.

The Health Advantages of a Plant-Based Diet

So, what is it about a plant-based diet that makes it so effective at achieving the health benefits discussed above? In part, it is the fifty nutrients and thousands of phytochemicals that plants provide, including antioxidants and fiber. It is also the lack of certain compounds in plants, such as cholesterol. A more detailed discussion of these components follows.

Phytonutrients

Phyto means "plant," so phytonutrients are nutrients that come only from plants. There are tens of thousands of plant nutrients. These compounds may be identified as antioxidants, flavonoids, phytonutrients, flavones, isoflavones, catechins, anthocyanidins, isothyocyanates, carotenoids, allyl sulfides, polyphenols, and resveratrol. Most people are familiar with the term "antioxidants" but don't understand why they are so beneficial. I like to use the analogy of making a fire. We put wood into the fireplace as fuel. We light a match, and, in combination with oxygen, we get what we want: a fire that creates light and heat. But, we also get some by-products that are harmful—in this case, ash, soot, and smoke.

Well, it is not much different in the body. We put food into our bodies as our fuel. Upon digestion, the compounds in the food interact with oxygen to create what we want: energy, in the form of calories, to perform our daily activities. But we also get some by-products that are harmful—in this case, free-radical electrons. These electrons act just like their name implies: they are free and they are radical. Free radicals are unstable electrons that bombard the body, causing damage to our DNA (mutation and cancer), aging (wrinkles), and inflammation, all of which underlie the vast majority of our chronic-disease states.

Now, of course, I always thought of Berkeley as the home of the original free radical, but in fact the production of free radicals has occurred naturally in the body since the beginning of humankind. Collectively, this process is called oxidation, or oxidative stress, and is the result of everyday activities, such as breathing, eating, exposure to the sun, toxins, pollution, stress, and even exercise. In fact, every cell in our body takes ten thousand hits of oxidative stress per day! What few people realize is that exercising can produce ten times as much oxidative stress because they take in more oxygen when they work out.

The only thing we can do to protect ourselves from oxidative stress is to consume more antioxidants. "Anti-" means "against," so antioxidants fight against oxidation, thereby protecting the cells. Antioxidants donate electrons to the free radicals, thereby stabilizing them so that they don't damage the body. Where do we get antioxidants? From plants, especially raw fruits and vegetables, which is why consuming enough fruits and vegetables is a cornerstone of the dietary recommendations of health organizations like the American Heart Association, the American Cancer Society, and the Academy of Nutrition and Dietetics. It is well recognized, for example, that people who consume five or more servings of fruits and vegetables each day have a significantly reduced risk of cancer than those who consume only two servings a day. In fact, it seems that the more fruits and vegetables one eats, the better that person's health status. That is one of the reasons why national health campaigns have moved from "5 a Day for Better Health" to "Fruits & Veggies: More Matters" as their slogan, with the recommendation to get between seven and thirteen servings or more per day. As I noted in chapter 5, there's no upper limit when it comes to these powerful plants. Following a plant-based diet will greatly increase the chances that you will meet these recommendations. That said, the reality is that fewer than 10 percent of American adults consume even the minimum number of recommended servings per day. As such, including a

whole-food, plant-based supplement like JuicePlus+ in your daily routine may be helpful.

Even though my family eats better than most, I find great comfort in knowing that we are consuming this particular supplement each and every day. That's because Juice Plus+ is whole food based nutrition, including juice powder concentrates from 30 different fruits, vegetables and grains, and is the most widely research nutrition supplement in the world. It's not a multivitamin, but a convenient, effective, affordable way to help bridge the gap between what we should eat and what we do eat every day. Even the most staunch nutritionist and mom—like yours truly—can use a little help when it comes to ensuring the most optimal levels of plant-based nutrition.

Fiber

Dietary fiber consists of more than a dozen structural and storage components in plants that enzymes in the human stomach and intestinal tract can't digest. There are two primary types of fiber: soluble and insoluble. Soluble fiber dissolves into a rather gummy substance. By binding fatty substances in the digestive tract, it helps lower blood cholesterol. It also slows the absorption of carbohydrates and thereby helps normalize blood glucose and insulin levels, crucial in managing diabetes and heart disease. Soluble fiber is found mainly in legumes, barley, brown rice, oats and

oat bran, fruits (especially apples, plums, citrus, strawberries, and blueberries), and vegetables (such as carrots, split peas, and corn). Insoluble fiber does not dissolve in water but rather holds on to it. By adding bulk to the diet, it helps suppress the appetite by slowing the absorption of nutrients. It softens stool and keeps the bowels moving smoothly, helping to prevent or treat constipation and prevent the development of diverticulosis and diverticulitis. Insoluble fiber also reduces the risk of colon cancer by moving toxic substances, potential cancer causing agents, more quickly through the digestive tract and diluting their concentration. Insoluble fiber is found primarily in whole-wheat products, especially wheat bran, and other whole grains.

Epidemiologic studies that emphasize the ability of fiber to protect against cardiovascular disease indicate that adults should consume twenty-five to forty grams of fiber per day. Some recommendations

a full menu of refined carbohydrates, including blueberry muffins, cinnamon rolls, scones, donuts, bagels, banana bread, morning buns, croissants, and coffee cake. Our society's ever-increasing fiber deficiency is partly attributable to the fact that refined flour doesn't spoil as quickly as whole grain flour, since the "alive" part has been taken out of it. Creating products with refined flours makes it easier

reach fifty grams per day, an amount many vegetarians easily and safely consume. For children, the recommended level is the child's age plus five grams per day. It is suggested that five to ten grams of one's total fiber intake be soluble fiber.

Unfortunately, the average fiber intake for Americans is only fifteen grams per day, which is the primary reason more than half the country is constipated. Highly processed and depleted in fiber, our Westernized way of eating is running us ragged. Walk into any Starbucks, and you will find

for food companies to produce mass quantities of packaged food more quickly. This process of stripping wheat of its nutritious compounds—the germ and endosperm—renders refined flour less nutritious, containing significantly less fiber, protein, B vitamins, and calcium than whole grain flour. The bad rap carbs have gotten in recent years, combined with a recent focus on protein, hasn't helped matters either. Too many people have cut out carbohydrates altogether, not just the processed ones, thereby severely minimizing their intake of fiber.

The planet has set our table with plenty of high-fiber foods, and we don't need to do anything complicated to get an adequate amount of fiber back into our diets—we simply need to eat the foods already available to us. By consuming lots and lots of fresh fruits and vegetables, making half the grains you eat whole grains, and eating beans—such as pinto, black, and garbanzo beans—more often, you should be able to meet the recommended fiber levels for optimal health. Including a plant-based smoothie or snack bar once a day also provides a quick and easy way to help attain this goal.

When considering what foods contain fiber, we can answer this question with the answer to another question: "Does the food come from an animal or a plant?" If it comes from an animal, it does *not* contain dietary fiber. If it comes from a plant—fruits, vegetables, beans, nuts, seeds, and whole grains—it *does* contain dietary fiber. Nearly all plant foods make some contribution toward our total dietary fiber intake, though some provide more than others. For example, a cup of raspberries provides 8.4 grams of dietary fiber, whereas a cup of blueberries provides 3.9 grams. How many grams of fiber does an egg provide? Zero! Nada! None! Why not? Because it comes from an animal. The same is true for a cup of milk, a piece of salmon, and a chicken breast. When it comes to getting fiber, stick with plants!

Saturated Fat and Cholesterol

While plants contain many compounds that do wonderful things for the body, they also shine in the sense of what they do *not* provide, such as cholesterol, or provide in very small amounts, such as saturated fat. Though "fat" is an emotionally charged word, it is essential to your health and diet. Fats supply "essential" fatty acids, which are required for the development of several hormone-like compounds, help maintain healthy skin and hair, transport fat-soluble vitamins through the bloodstream, regulate blood cholesterol levels, and serve as storage for the body's excess calories. The problem is that the vast majority of us are consuming too much of it and the wrong types of it.

It is the position of the American Academy of Nutrition and Dietetics (AND) and Dietitians of Canada (DC) that dietary fat for the adult population should provide 20 to 35 percent of calories and emphasize a reduction in saturated fat and trans fats (both of which increase the risk of heart disease) and an increase in omega-3 polyunsaturated fats. On average, vegans consume less than 30 percent of their calories from fat, which is just a little less than the average nonvegan, although some studies put the average nonvegan intake at 40 percent. What makes the significant differences in their disease rates is the *type* of fat consumed. Most of the saturated fat in the Standard American Diet (SAD) comes from meat and dairy foods. Some plant foods, like olives and nuts, are high in total fat but generally contain healthy poly- and monounsaturated fats, which actually help prevent heart disease and are low in saturated fat. Further, plants are void of hazardous trans fats, because such fats are artificially made. Essentially, trans fats are naturally occurring fats that are blasted with hydrogen—hence the term "hydrogenated fat." We are not intended to ingest these manufactured fats. The body does not know how to handle them, and they therefore increase the risk of disease.

Cholesterol is a white, waxy substance that is present in body tissue and circulates in the blood. While it is natural and necessary to make important bodily functions possible, including the production of hormones, we do not need to consume any cholesterol in order for our bodies to carry out these functions, because our bodies already make all that we need.

Different from the cholesterol that is found in foods, two types of cholesterol exist in the blood: high-density lipoprotein (HDL) and low-density lipoprotein (LDL). A high level of HDL, commonly referred to as "good cholesterol," is strongly linked to a decreased risk of heart disease, due to the fact that HDLs carry cholesterol away from the arteries. Less waxy buildup in the arteries translates to better blood flow. HDL cholesterol also protects the heart through its potential antioxidant and anti-inflammatory effects.

Low-density lipoprotein (LDL), or "bad" cholesterol, on the other hand, contributes to the development of atherosclerosis, a slow, progressive accumulation of fatty deposits within the arteries that leads to heart attack and stroke. When there is more LDL in the bloodstream than the body needs, the excess is deposited within the walls of the arteries, including the coronary arteries, which transport blood to and from the heart. Over time, this buildup narrows the area through which blood can flow. When LDL accumulates, it becomes oxidized, and that oxidization leads to inflammation. When blood pressure increases, there is an increased risk that a piece of the plaque will break away and travel in the blood and eventually get stuck in one of the vessels, prohibiting blood flow to an important area—the heart or brain, for example. Once such an area to which blood is not flowing becomes oxygen deprived, the body will not be viable. In short, no oxygen means no life.

An expert panel from the American College of Cardiology and the American Heart Association released new cholesterol guidelines in November 2013. The recommendation to adopt a plant-based diet that is low in saturated fat and sodium, physical activity, and a healthy body weight remains the same. What has changed is that there is less emphasis on blood cholesterol levels, because no studies have assessed the benefits of reaching the previously recommended targets. That said, it is still wise to have a fasting lipid panel (total cholesterol,

LDL and HDL cholesterol, and triglycerides) and to have some understanding of what it means.

Many of you probably take these blood tests routinely; others may have never had this panel done. Even if you are not overweight, do not assume that your levels are healthy. My father's experience illustrates this fact. Thin as a rail, he would consume two McDonald's Big Macs, a Filet-O-Fish, and french fries in one sitting and never gain weight. But it was because his arteries grew clogged over time that he ended up having heart surgery so early on in his life. He was actually quite fortunate, in that they recognized his problem—because he was having angina, or chest pain—before he suffered a stroke or heart attack.

Remember that while we do burn calories, we do not burn cholesterol. Cholesterol stays with us, building up in our arteries over time. It's one reason why amazingly fit athletes will drop dead of a heart attack: they burn off so many calories through exercise that they can eat a lot of food. But many of those foods come from an animal or contain ingredients from an animal and thus contribute cholesterol to a system that doesn't require it. Excess cholesterol builds up over time. Tragically, we are now finding children as young as ten years old have the arteries of forty-five-year-olds. Our arteries are the vessels through which blood transports nutrients and oxygen throughout the body. When these vessels become clogged with plaque—fatty deposits caused by both cholesterol and saturated fat—the space through which blood can flow is reduced to a much tighter area. This restriction naturally leads to high blood pressure, which in turn can cause either a hemorrhage (where a blood vessel ruptures) or a

stroke (where a piece of the plaque breaks off the arterial wall and then blocks the passage of blood). Again, we do not need to consume cholesterol in order to get what our body needs. Any excess that we do consume is stored in our arteries. Unfortunately, the number one symptom of heart disease is death. That's why cholesterol has been called the Silent Killer.

Is cholesterol found in food? Yes, but only in food that comes from animals, e.g. cows, pigs, chicken, turkey, and, yes, fish, too, as well as from the products they produce, such as milk and eggs. Determining which foods contain cholesterol is the exact opposite of how we can tell if a food contains fiber: Foods from an animal *do* contain cholesterol and *do not* contain fiber. Foods from a plant *do not* contain cholesterol—not even those high in fat, like avocados, olives, and nuts—and *do* contain fiber. Cholesterol, unlike fat, is not visible on animal food. Unlike skin that can be removed from a chicken leg, for example, cholesterol is located in the membranes and around the cells of the lean portion of the animal flesh. As such, eating leaner animal foods does not result in lower blood cholesterol levels. The best way to drop your blood cholesterol levels is by reducing animal foods in your diet or eliminating them altogether. While this is in part due to the overall reduction of cholesterol, it is primarily due to the minimization of saturated fat which has been shown to raise cholesterol levels.

Is There Anything Missing?

A perception exists that vegetarian diets are deficient in important nutrients, including protein, calcium, iron, and vitamin B_{12}. However, data from recent National Health and Nutrition Examination Survey analyses, as well as from previous population studies, characterizing a lacto-ovo-vegetarian dietary pattern, do not entirely support these concerns. All plant foods contain protein, although fruit contains very little. Most of the concern around protein in vegan diets stems from a misunderstanding about "complete" and "incomplete" proteins.

I like to use language as an analogy to explain how proteins are made. There are twenty-six letters in the alphabet. We use those letters to create an infinite number of words and sentences that help us to communicate and thus make things happen. If there were a limited supply of vowels to work with, we wouldn't be able to say nearly as much; not even close. Similarly, proteins are made up of amino acids, some of which the body makes and some of which must be supplied by the food we eat. The ones we need to consume are called essential amino acids. Plant foods like grains, beans, and nuts are generally low in at least one essential amino acid, and therefore "incomplete." Notice I didn't say *missing* an amino acid—contrary to popular belief, all plant foods that contain protein do, in fact, contain all the essential amino acids. It's just that beans, for example, have a low percentage of the essential amino acid methionine, while grains have a low percentage of the essential amino acid lysine. But when eaten together, they provide a healthy dose of *all* the essential amino acids. There's a reason the earth serves up such a wide variety!

In the early 1970s, much discussion occurred around the need to eat those complementary foods in the same meal, but now we know that "food combining" isn't necessary for this purpose, because the body maintains its own storage of essential amino acids. As my registered-dietitian friend Virginia Messina says in her book *Vegan for Life*, "You could even get enough protein and all the essential amino acids by eating just one type of food like pinto beans. You'd need to eat a lot of them, though—about four cups per day." Of course, that sounds boring and so isn't recommended, but you get the idea. And any concern that a vegan diet does not provide enough protein is without just cause. Most Americans eat more than twice as much protein as the body requires, most of which is provided by animal foods, which, again, is one of the reasons why we are faced with so many health challenges.

Some people say that their bodies just "have to have" meat and claim to feel terrible when they stop eating it. However, these physical symptoms may be merely a sign of detoxification, rather than a sign that these people actually can't live without meat. Just as a person often experiences headaches, irritability, and other signs of withdrawal when giving up caffeine, nicotine, or alcohol, one can also experience unpleasant symptoms when withdrawing from eating meat. Any departure from an established dietary habit is likely to trigger some type of symptoms. While potentially unpleasant, this is a short-term state that will give way to long-term benefits. At the end of the day, protein, whether it comes from an animal or a plant, is made up of amino acids. If we use our analogy of language, animal flesh (rib, thigh, breast, wing, whatever) is like a sentence made up of different letters. The differences between animals and plants are what accompany the protein. Animal protein is accompanied by cholesterol and saturated fat but not fiber, whereas plant protein is accompanied by fiber without the cholesterol and saturated fat.

Calcium and iron are two minerals that are often of concern to those embarking on a plant-based diet, because calcium is generally associated with dairy products and iron is generally associated with meat. But most nuts, seeds, and dark leafy greens contribute calcium and iron to the diet. While the relationship between calcium, protein, and bone health remains conflicted, it is worth noting that when you follow a plant-based diet, your system is more likely to be more alkaline, or less acidic, because you're both eating more fruits and vegetables and consuming less protein. That's a good thing!

Acidity and alkalinity are measured by the pH scale, which goes from 0 (most acidic) to 14 (most alkaline); 7 is neutral. A diet that increases the acidity of the body is generally considered to be unhealthy—perhaps even the cause of most diseases, from cancer and arthritis to depression and diabetes. Despite the plethora of articles supporting these claims, most are not well-founded. Nonetheless, there is a kernel of truth within them, particularly where bone health is concerned.

The body keeps its acid balance in the normal range in several ways, including excretion of acid by the kidneys and acid reduction via exhalation of carbon dioxide. The body also neutralizes the blood's acidity by releasing calcium compounds, which are alkaline. Of course, our bones are a storehouse of calcium and laboratory studies have shown that an acid-boosting diet can, indeed, cause bones to release calcium to assist this effort, thereby weakening them. People who eat lots of fruits and vegetables—which are alkaline-forming foods—tend to have stronger bones, and studies have found that the blood-pressure-lowering DASH diet, which is rich in fruits and vegetables, helps reduce calcium loss. What about the effect of other foods? Nuts, legumes, some grains (such as rice, pasta, and corn flakes), hard cheeses, and eggs increase acidity; milk and yogurt apparently do not. Sodas, because of the phosphorous they contain, are also high on the acid scale, which is why some studies have linked a very high soda consumption to weaker bones.

There is controversy, however, about how significant the effect of an acid-boosting diet is on bones and the risk of osteoporosis, especially in people who consume adequate amounts of calcium. Since the kidneys help reduce acidity, and kidney function does decline with age, some researchers believe that an acid-boosting diet may help explain some of the bone loss in older people. But so many factors affect bone health—including genetics, physical activity, and many nutrients—that it's hard to tease out the effect of an acid-boosting diet. That all said, the alkaline contribution of fruits and vegetables is just one more amongst many reasons to consume them.

In regard to iron, there are two types: heme and nonheme. Heme iron is much better absorbed than nonheme iron and is found in red meat, poultry, and seafood. Many people use this fact as a reason to eat such animal foods. However, the body is less able to regulate heme iron, and excess levels contribute to free radical formation. And while the research remains inconclusive, excessive levels of iron may contribute to increased risk of chronic disease, including certain cancers, heart disease, and kidney damage.

Nonheme iron is available from plants, including leafy greens, beans, and oatmeal. In fact, most plants contain at least some nonheme iron—yet another reason to enjoy the wide variety of plants that the planet offers. Consider that an ounce of sesame seeds provides about three times the amount of iron as an ounce of beef liver. To increase your iron absorption, include foods with vitamin C with your meals. That can mean tomato sauce on pasta, orange juice with cereal, and salsa with a taco, as a few of countless examples. This practice helps prevent iron deficiency while also protecting against the pro-oxidative effects of excess iron. Obtaining iron from plants instead of animals also protects us against the potential negative effects of heme iron while providing the additional benefits of avoiding cholesterol and saturated fat. Vitamin B_{12}, required for cell division, red-blood-cell formation, metabolism, and the protection of nerve fibers, is made from bacteria and thus is available only in animal foods. So what's a vegan to do, imperfect or not? Take a B_{12} supplement! It's a simple and small price to pay for gaining so many positive health benefits.

Transformation Requires Synergy

One of the most exciting things about nutrition is that it constantly shows us how the sacred works all things together for good. First of all, within all the foods that the universe provides there exists every nutrient needed for your most vibrant expression of health. It's not necessary to manufacture a single food. In fact, it is the official position of the American Academy of Nutrition and Dietetics is that most healthy people can get all the nutrients they need from food in a well planned diet, and that the best nutrition based strategy for promoting optimal health and reducing the risk of chronic disease is to wisely choose a wide variety of nutrient-rich foods.

However, most people realize that they do not consume enough healthy food, particularly fruits and vegetables. So what do we do? Well, at least 50 percent of Americans take a multivitamin every day, at a cost of over $20 billion per year. The use of dietary supplements in general, and nutrient supplements in particular, is prevalent and growing in the United States, but multivitamins don't work and can in fact be hazardous to your health.

First, foods contain substances that are not available from nutritional supplements. Supplements contain only those nutrients that scientists have discovered and have been able to extract and put into capsules, tablets, gels, and powders. But there are thousands of important compounds that simply have not been discovered

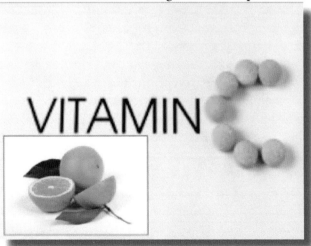

yet, or that scientists haven't figured out how to isolate and put in a pill. A well-known saying in nutritional circles is "If science could create a pill that gave us all the vitamins and minerals we need, the only problem would be swallowing it!" It's important to remember that supplements are just that—they are intended to supplement the nutritional value of your diet, not be its primary source.

Second, food provides the synergy that many nutrients require for efficient use by the body. The term "synergy" refers to the action of two or more substances or organisms coming together to achieve an effect that each is incapable of achieving alone. In the context of restoring the spiritual aspect of eating, theological doctrine refers to synergy as "the regeneration that is brought about by a combination of the human will and sacred grace working together." That's cocreation!

While the RDA for vitamin C is sixty milligrams (enough to prevent scurvy and other deficiency diseases), much higher levels are often recommended for optimal health. However, since vitamin C is a water-soluble vitamin and the body can absorb only about two hundred milligrams at one time, intakes above this amount literally go down the drain through urine. In the case of supplements providing high doses of vitamin C, this is wasted money. To underscore the difference between isolated nutrients and whole food, the small amount of vitamin C in an apple, about six milligrams, along with the total amount of antioxidants, is as effective at reducing oxidative stress as 1,300 milligrams of isolated vitamin C. That's the power of synergy! Our previous discussion about how we absorb more heme iron

when we consume it along with vitamin C provides another example, as does the fact that carotenoids, like the precursor to vitamin A, are better absorbed when consumed with fat, since many are fat soluble. I imagine there are countless other examples of food synergy that have yet to be discovered. By eating a wide variety of whole plant foods, we optimize our chances of benefiting from them all.

One of the most significant studies to awaken researchers and health care providers to the importance of food synergy is the Beta-Carotene and Retinol Efficacy Trial (CARET). Because observational studies suggest that people eating more fruits and vegetables rich in beta-carotene and retinol have lower rates of lung cancer, researchers wanted to test the effects of such natural compounds in isolated form, so they administered high dosages of vitamins to more than eighteen thousand people at high risk for cancer and death from smoking and asbestos exposure. Half of the subjects were given an "intervention" of vitamins, while the other half received a placebo (no vitamin intervention). During the study, researchers found that those given the vitamins had a 28 percent increase in lung cancer, a 17 percent increase in death, and an increased risk of cardiovascular disease, compared with the group that did not receive the vitamins. Because the trial presented no clear evidence of benefit and substantial evidence of possible harm, the researchers terminated it in 1996, twenty-one months earlier than planned, and took all subjects off the vitamin intervention.

CARET is just one of an increasing number of studies that have found isolated vitamins to be ineffective and dangerous. Fortunately, the media is getting the word out! This standpoint is supported by *UC Berkeley's School of Public Health's Wellness Report 2016: Dietary Supplements*, which states that many popular nutrition supplements are not as effective as had been thought, including our daily multivitamin pill. Further, the US government neither regulates supplements nor tests them for safety or effectiveness. Supplement manufacturers are not required to list exact nutrients and quantities of nutrients on their labels, nor are they required to prove a product's safety and efficacy before they release it into the marketplace. The word "natural" on a label does not mean that the product is safe; furthermore, false claims like "boosts stamina," "arouses sexual desire," and "enhances muscle tone" *can* be listed on the label. Finally, the FDA does not require supplements to carry warning labels regarding any potential side effects, which include dizziness, nausea, blurred vision, muscle cramps, headache, constipation, difficulty breathing, insomnia, decreased libido, and tremors.

What's behind these findings? Essentially, the constituents of food are most biologically active when they are provided in whole-food form and can be ineffective and toxic when isolated. Just as an orchestra is composed of musicians playing various instruments, so is the body served by food providing various nutrients. If you were to isolate a violin from the musician, there would be no sound. Similarly, isolating a single nutrient from food does not allow it to serve the body as intended. Evolutionarily, humans tell each other about foods that make them sick, not individual nutrients. Dietary supplements containing isolated vitamins or minerals do not have the same beneficial effects as food itself. Consider that the average multivitamin supplement contains thirty-one nutrients. Consuming a multivitamin is like having thirty pieces of a ten-thousand-piece puzzle—can you put the puzzle together? No. And having high doses of a single nutrient, like vitamin C, is like having one thousand identical puzzle pieces. Again, can you assemble the puzzle? No.

What we need to solve the puzzle is thousands of unique pieces that fit together. In human life, what the body needs is what a variety of plants, especially fruit and vegetables, provide: tens of thousands of unique compounds that work together synergistically. That said, with so few people meeting even the minimum number of daily recommended servings of fruits and vegetables, I strongly recommend including a whole food supplement like JuicePlus+ in your regime. In my opinion, with a growing collection of independent research on its safety and effectiveness, it stands as one of our most viable public health nutrition efforts. There are special cases in which taking an isolated nutrient is recommended, such as B_{12} supplements for vegans. But generally, our bodies assimilate nutrients most effectively when we eat them in their natural state—whole foods.

❧

More Reasons to Be Imperfectly Vegan

In addition to health, the decision to be Imperfectly Vegan can be based on other important values as well, such as limiting cruelty to animals and preserving the planet. His Holiness the Dalai Lama says, "I have been particularly concerned with the sufferings of chickens for many years. It was the death of a chicken that finally strengthened my resolve to become vegetarian. These days, when I see a row of plucked chickens hanging in a meat shop, it hurts. I find it unacceptable that violence is the basis of some of our food habits." Beloved author and activist Alice Walker says, "Animals of the world exist for their own reasons. They were not made for humans any more than blacks were made for whites or women for men."

I find that more and more young people are turning to a plant-based diet because of an experience of visiting a slaughterhouse or factory farm. Health isn't much of a concern to them at their age, but witnessing violence against animals makes an impact. Being Imperfectly Vegan also allows you to support the planet, which is in desperate need of our help. A 2005 study by the University of Chicago found that one person switching from a meat-based diet to a plant-based diet could save about the same amount of carbon dioxide as trading in a Toyota Camry for a Toyota Prius! That's because raising cattle requires about eighty calories of fossil fuel to cultivate one food calorie, whereas only two calories of fossil fuel are required to cultivate one food calorie of grains, fruits, and vegetables. Furthermore, cattle belch methane, a greenhouse gas that is twenty times more potent than carbon dioxide. And—as if we really need another reason—by being green, you'll keep more green in your wallet! While prices vary widely, an average pound of nonorganic factory-farmed ground beef costs around $5 and a pound of chicken breasts $4. A pound of canned beans, in contrast, costs less than $1. The difference is even greater when you purchase high quality, organic, grassfed beef. One couple figured they could save $2,000–3,000 per year by eating a plant-based diet. And, last but certainly not least, being Imperfectly Vegan is fun, easy, and delicious!

గు

That pretty much takes care of things. The confirmed health advantages of vegetarian nutrition are well documented. Frankly, the evidence thus far, combined with common sense, should be enough for us to move forward. We can choose to invest in our health now or invest in treatment later. We do not need to spend so much money on seeking cures for cancer if we can turn our focus to prevention; we already have everything we need to create optimal well-being, because the earth has put it right in front of us. We just can't see it anymore through our forest of processed foods. Of course, these advantages are greatest the earlier one adopts an optimal diet, but it is never too late to improve your situation, given that the body is constantly undergoing transformation. And what's so wonderful about this simple approach is that by focusing your diet on plants, you will feel yourself becoming more and more aligned with higher principles. Your integrity as a human on this planet will increase, and your radiance will expand. As time passes and newer generations eat in a way that honors our individual, communal, and environmental well-being, we will experience a positive shift toward greater and greater levels of human wholeness and planetary healing.

CHAPTER SEVEN

Gathering Ingredients

THE WORD "GATHERING" takes us back to a time of hunters and gatherers. Hunters sought meat to eat. Gatherers sought plant foods to consume. When we go to our modern-day grocery stores, many of the forty thousand–plus different things to eat there are not really food at all. Food advertising has led us to eat things that look like food but are filled with artificial sweeteners, colors, fillers, and isolated nutrients. Calcium, for example, is now added to some sodas to unsuccessfully make up for the calcium withdrawal from bones that drinking soda can cause. No wonder so many of these manufactured "foodstuffs" make us "sick, fat, and nearly dead"! We are human beings dependent upon food for life living on a planet that serves up enough for everyone. Let's gather ingredients wisely.

The first step in doing so is recognizing that it is more important than ever to eat organic foods. Over the last one hundred years, the use of pesticides, herbicides, and fungicides has increased. In the mid-1990s, Monsanto quietly slipped genetically modified organisms, or GMOs, into our food supply and kicked off what would become an ever more heated political debate on the subject. Facts and opinions about GMOs vary widely, so I encourage you to do your own research in order to make an informed determination for yourself about your stance on GMOs. The following information represents my personal take.

When Monsanto began genetically modifying crops, it started by altering soy, salmon, sugar beets, canola oil, and other foods to withstand glyphosate, a chemical in the corporation's herbicide Roundup. By 1998, approximately eighteen million acres were planted with genetically engineered Roundup Ready soybeans, modified to contain a bacterial gene that confers Roundup tolerance.

When insects consumed these plants containing glyphosate, their stomachs exploded. Thus, only insects that were resistant to Roundup could survive. To manage these superbugs, the industry added 2,4-D, which is in Agent Orange, a chemical that the US military used as part of its chemical warfare program Operation Ranch Hand during the Vietnam War from, 1961 to 1971.

Upon attending the 5th International Vegetarian Conference in 2015, I was startled to learn of research indicating that animals who consume these GMO foods are experiencing increasing rates of cancer, endocrine damage, and infertility. And because the pests that are able to survive their use are more resistant, chemical companies have developed stronger and more toxic pesticides to kill them. These toxic chemicals find their way into the foods we eat, the air we breathe, and the water we drink, thereby increasing our risk of cancer and other health problems.

Another chemical, which has been sprayed on corn crops that provide the sugar in almost all of our processed and fast foods, is called *Bacillus thuringiensis*, or Bt. As with Roundup, when insects ate plants sprayed with Bt, their stomachs exploded, thereby enabling farmers to protect their crops. But it was not economical to spray Bt on the plants, and so the next thing the industry did was to splice DNA from one plant species into another. Though Bt manufacturers assert that it has no harmful effects

on humans, consumers should be very skeptical of such claims. Until the USDA requires non-GMO labeling, the safest way to ensure that you're buying foods that have not been genetically modified and/or treated with pesticides, herbicides, and fungicides is to buy organic items as often as possible.

According to the National Organic Standards Board, products labeled "organic" must contain at least 95 percent organic ingredients. The other 5 percent (excluding water and salt) must be nonagricultural substances on an approved list, or nonorganically produced products that are not available commercially in organic form. These products may display the USDA seal.

Products labeled "made with organic ingredients" are processed food products (cereals, pastas, breads, canned goods, etc.) that must contain at least 70 percent organic ingredients. These products may *not* use the USDA seal. Processed products that contain fewer than 70 percent organic ingredients can list those ingredients as organic but cannot be labeled "organic."

Another simple way to avoid GMOs is by eating as much locally grown food as possible. According to a 2007 poll conducted by the Leopold Center for Sustainable Agriculture at Iowa State University, Americans feel better about buying foods produced domestically than overseas and believe that food grown locally is healthier than food shipped across the country. By extension, food grown close to home is even more beneficial than that grown across the country. Following is a list of options for eating sustainably, beginning with those closest to home and progressing to those farthest away.

Start a Garden in Your Backyard

One of the best ways to access healthy, fresh, organic food is to grow it yourself. Doing so puts you in control of how your food is farmed and almost negates the need to travel for your food. There are websites that can lead you through the how-to steps of creating a garden. And if you are really motivated to help heal the planet, learn about permaculture, which works with native landscapes and wildlife to create sustainable systems that can even help to renew the land.

While I clearly have a strong appreciation for fresh fruits and vegetables, I do not have a green thumb. What has worked best for me is a system called TowerGarden by JuicePlus+, available for

home use since 2011. Besides being easy and fun, TowerGarden is good for the environment. Because no dirt is involved, it uses 90 percent less water than what would be required to grow the same amount of produce in land, and because it's vertical, it uses 90 percent less land and can even fit on small porches. The need for organic and conventional pesticides is also reduced or eliminated, since there's no dirt (and, thus, fewer bugs), and because the tonic and mineral solution helps the plants to grow healthy and strong such that they are better able to protect themselves from plant pests and disease. Further, the TowerGarden reduces your carbon footprint because it virtually eliminates shipping and storage of produce.

One of my very favorite aspects about this system and any backyard garden is that there is no waste. I hate throwing away produce that goes bad before it gets eaten, which can happen a lot with organic produce. With TowerGarden, I simply walk into my backyard to pick just as much as I need—whether a handful of greens (kale, spinach, parsley, bok choy) to add to my morning smoothie, mixed gourmet lettuces for a salad, or herbs for a cooked meal. It doesn't get faster or fresher than that. (For more information, visit https://lisacelebrates.towergarden.com.)

Join a Community Garden or Visit Your Local Farmers' Market

If you don't grow food in your own backyard, growing and purchasing food locally is the next best option. Joining a community garden and visiting your local farmers' market are two great ways to do so, because they share these important benefits:

- Local produce is higher in nutritional content, since it usually reaches the consumer within twenty-four hours of harvest.
- Local farmers offer produce varieties bred for taste and freshness, rather than for long distance shipping and long shelf life.
- Fresh produce sold locally is usually picked at its peak, when the nutrients are richest.
- Buying food near your home reduces the need for pesticides and other chemicals that are used to keep produce looking fresh longer.
- Conservation practices used on small gardens and farms, such as grassed waterways and wetlands, filter waterborne pollutants, reduce food contaminating pathogens, and improve water quality.
- Biological farming is more likely to promote healthy soil characterized by a high level of microbial biodiversity. Compost, cover crops, and crop rotations result in healthy soil that produces healthy plants.

I live in a small suburban town that is remarkably progressive about sustainability. In 2008, a small group of residents, including gardeners and educators, began developing plans for a community garden. In 2012, community members installed hoses, built planters, and planted produce from seed. Each member family may harvest produce from the garden to take home. In addition to providing fresh organic produce, the garden offers educational classes to the community, in which residents learn about such things as sustainable farming practices, their local habitat, and the medicinal qualities of native plants.

While not everyone has access to a farmers' market, they are becoming more and more present in various locations. Taking a trip to the farmers' market can feel like a field trip. In fact, I enjoy it so much that it has become a personal tradition for me to visit the farmers' market at the San Francisco Ferry Building on Mother's Day. When my kids were little, I would give them each $10 to purchase some new fruit or vegetable to try. What makes both community gardens and farmers' markets so special is that, in addition to providing wholesome nourishment for the body, they provide connection and community for the soul.

Visit Your Local Grocery Store

While we want to get our ingredients from the earth, there will be some things that we will need to pick up at the grocery store. All of the following can help make your shopping experience more efficient and fun:

- Bring a shopping list. This will save you time, energy, money, and calories!

- Don't shop on an empty stomach. Doing so can lead to fatigue, frustration, and impulse buying. Even if you're not hungry when you head out to the store, you may find your stomach grumbling in the middle of the bread aisle. Eat a piece of fruit or a small handful of nuts before shopping to minimize this risk.

- Bring your kids. Involving them in the decision making process may help them to make healthier food choices. Some stores have child-size grocery carts that add to the fun. Of course, taking children to establishments that offer lots of healthy foods is key. I used to take my boys to the Berkeley Bowl just for the adventure of it. We would walk up and down the produce aisles and, sure enough, they would ask for an apple or a peach. By the time they were four years old, they could name about twenty-five different fruits and vegetables.

- Avoid aisles that are loaded with processed foods that are stripped of valuable nutrition and more likely to contain added chemicals, sugar, and fat.

- Be cautious of processed, bagged, precut salad mixes. Because the ingredients are sourced from multiple farms, they increase the risk of food-borne illness through cross contamination. Processing precut produce increases the risk of bacterial contamination by cutting into the leafy greens and breaking the leaves' natural outer layer, opening pathways for contaminants. The sealed plastic bags in which salads are shipped may be an ideal environment for bacterial growth if they are not kept cold at all times.

- Follow a routine. Having a set day and time to shop can help you move through the store quickly. Consider going during off hours to avoid crowds or anytime you know you won't feel rushed.

How to Select Fruits and Vegetables

Whether you're picking produce straight from your home garden or community garden, selecting it at your local farmers' market, or shopping for it at the grocery store, certain guidelines for selecting produce apply across the board. Here are some tips on how to select the freshest, most delicious, and most nutritious fruits and vegetables:

- Follow the rainbow! As I mentioned in chapter 5, research increasingly shows that foods with color and rich flavor contain more phytonutrients that help prevent chronic disease and promote robust health. For example, blue and purple foods (like blueberries and grapes) contain resveratrol, a compound that helps promote cardiovascular wellness, while orange and yellow foods (like apricots and carrots) contain beta-carotene, which aids in the prevention of cancer. The deeper the color, the better. For example, when shopping for grapefruit and grapefruit juice, you should be aware that red pulp is more nutritious than yellow pulp because the red color is due to lycopene, which may help lower the risk of certain cancers, especially prostate. Similarly, dark green spinach is going to have more nutrients than pale green iceberg lettuce. It is no coincidence that the earth serves up fruits and vegetables covering the full color spectrum—we have not been created without the resources to sustain ourselves!

- Shop in season as much as possible.

- Purchase produce grown as close to home as possible. More and more grocery stores are posting information about where their produce was grown.

- Purchase a wide variety of fruits and vegetables. In the grocery store, do you habitually reach for the same items week after week? Try something new! Variety in your diet gives you more nutrients and keeps you and your family from getting stuck and bored in a food rut. Have you ever tried a longan, for example? It's a round, cherry-size fruit with a thick, nonedible brown shell. Inside, the white, juicy fruit, which surrounds a large black seed, is fragrant and sweet. What about a kumquat? These members of the citrus family look like small, olive-shaped oranges. They can be eaten with the peel on, either uncooked or cooked.

- Beware of perfect looking produce. It's usually a sign that it has been grown with pesticides.
- Buy organic as much as possible. For reasons we've already discussed, buying organic is the best way to avoid GMOs, as well as dangerous pesticides, fungicides, and herbicides. While some produce items, like bananas, avocados, and onion, are generally grown using fewer pesticides, there are some that should be purchased in organic form. Since 2004, the Environmental Working Group (EWG), a nonprofit advocacy agency, has released a list of the most pesticide-contaminated produce items, called the Dirty Dozen. While debunked by some, I find this list

to be informative. Because it changes from year to year, you can google it to get the most current recommendations. Organic produce tends to cost more, though this may change as consumers begin to consistently demand and purchase such foods. If you are on a tight budget, take an honest look at the foods you are purchasing and consider whether or not you would be better off investing in higher quality produce than something else. It is still better to consume conventional produce than no produce at all, and, again, given the increasing numbers of chemicals used on produce, go organic whenever possible.

How to Select Grains

As I mentioned in the previous chapter, one of the reasons we are lacking fiber is that it has been removed from our grains. One way to increase your fiber intake is to make sure at least half of the breads and grains you eat are *whole grain*. Whole-grain foods are made from the entire grain seed (usually called the kernel), which consists of the bran, germ, and endosperm. If the kernel has been cracked, crushed, or flaked, it must retain nearly the same relative proportions of bran, germ, and endosperm as the original grain to be called whole-grain.

Refined grains have undergone milling, which removes the bran and the germ. This process also removes much of the B vitamins, iron, and dietary fiber. Some refined grains are "enriched" or "fortified." Both of these terms indicate that nutrients—usually vitamins or minerals—were added to make a food more nutritious. "Enriched" means adding back nutrients that were lost during food processing. For example, B vitamins, lost when wheat is refined, are added back to white flour. "Fortified" means adding nutrients to food that weren't originally present. Most grain products are now fortified with folic acid to reduce the risk of certain birth defects.

When gathering whole grains, keep in mind that color isn't always a telltale sign. Bread can appear to be whole-grain when packaged in brown bags or when the bread itself is brown due to molasses or other added ingredients. A more accurate way to ensure that you're choosing whole-grain foods is to pick items that name at least one of the following in their ingredients list:

- amaranth
- brown rice
- buckwheat
- bulgur (cracked wheat)
- corn
- graham flour
- gluten-free oats
- kasha
- millet
- popcorn
- quinoa
- sorghum
- tapioca
- taro
- teff
- triticale
- whole-grain barley
- whole oats
- whole rye
- whole wheat
- wild rice

Foods are usually *not* whole-grain products if they are labeled with these terms:
- Multigrain
- Stone-ground
- 100 percent wheat
- Cracked wheat
- Seven-grain
- Bran

Use a "Nutrition Facts" label, such as the one in the example below, to help choose whole-grain products with a higher percent Daily Value (% DV) for fiber. The % DV for fiber is a good clue as to the amount of whole grain in the product.

Increasingly, more and more people are claiming to be intolerant of or allergic to gluten, a protein

Which grain food is higher in fiber?

Use "Nutrition Facts" label to help choose whole grain products with a higher % Daily Value (%DV) for fiber. The %DV for fiber is a good clue to the amount of whole grain in the product. Cereals that are good fiber sources supply at least 2.5 grams of fiber per serving.

'A' is higher in dietary fiber as shown by both the number of grams of fiber per serving and by the % Daily Value.

found in wheat, barley, oats, and rye. This is a rather controversial subject among health professionals, given that celiac disease, an autoimmune disease that causes a permanent intolerance of gluten, affects just 1 percent of the population. Part of this inquiry comes from the fact that some people seem to have trouble with wheat products produced in the United States but not with those produced in other countries. As such, some question whether US wheat crops are being sprayed with glyphosate or perhaps are genetically modified or something else. There is growing speculation that the increase in genetically modified organisms is leading more people to experience leaky-gut syndrome, in which the integrity of the intestinal wall is weakened such that unrecognizable compounds are passing through it, thereby triggering an allergic reaction. This idea, however, has not been adequately substantiated. As such, if you suspect that you may be gluten intolerant, the best approach is to eliminate gluten-containing foods from your diet for about thirty days to determine how you feel as a result. Because gluten is often used in sauces, flavorings, and flavor enhancers and as a binder or filler in medications, vitamins, and supplements, adhering to a strict gluten-free diet requires eliminating these products as well. The good news is that an increasing number of gluten-free products are available at most grocery and health food stores today.

How to Select Seeds, Nuts, and Legumes

Seeds, nuts, and legumes are whole foods that makes shopping for them easy. When selecting these foods, remember the following:

- Buy these foods from bins whenever possible, since this will prevent the unnecessary purchase of plastics and containers that add to landfills. You will also be more likely to purchase just the amount you need and will thereby avoid having to throw away any excess that has gone bad over time. This method almost always costs less, too!
- Choose unsalted varieties to avoid excess sodium.

- When buying peanut or other nut butters, go for the "all natural" or 'old-fashioned' varieties to avoid hydrogenated fat and even added sugars.

How to Select Fats and Oils

While fats and oils provide nutrition and flavor, they are recommended in small amounts, since they are high in fat and calories. When selecting oil for purchase, consider the following:

- When purchasing oils, look for polyunsaturated oils, such as corn oil, or monounsaturated oils, such as olive oil.
- Extra-virgin, virgin, fine, and ungraded olive oils are the same nutritionally.
- "Light" olive oil is also the same—not lower in calories, just lighter in flavor and/or color than other olive oils.

How to Select Canned and Frozen Foods

For certain foods and in some seasons, canned and frozen foods can be very practical. You may even can or freeze your own homegrown produce for use year-round. But when you are shopping for such items, it is important to check their labels, as unwanted sugar, salt, fat, and preservatives can easily be added. Bear in mind the following information when shopping for canned and frozen foods:

- Fruits packed in their own juices have less sugar than fruits packed in heavy syrup.
- Frozen fruits and veggies are packed at their ripest state—so they are equal to fresh produce in nutrient content.
- Canned soups and canned vegetables are often loaded with added sodium. Be wary!
- Reconsider canned corn. The heat processing used to prepare canned corn actually boosts levels of antioxidants and other healthy phytochemicals in sweet corn. Heating corn, whether on the cob or

in the can, has a similar effect.
- Be careful if you purchase processed frozen meals, as they can vary greatly in nutrient content and often provide much more sodium, fat, and calories than are recommended for a single meal.
- As with fruits and vegetables in general, it is also important to look for organic varieties as much as possible—including when you are shopping for canned legumes.

How to Select Vegetarian Ingredients

A vegetarian diet can include foods that may be unfamiliar to you. If you're unsure of what to look for when shopping for vegetarian ingredients, the following list compiled by Vegetarian Nutrition, a dietetic practice group of the Academy of Nutrition and Dietetics, may be helpful. It might feel awkward the first time you purchase any of these items, but the process will become easy and natural with practice:

- Nutritional yeast: a powdered or flaked product that gives a cheese-like flavor to recipes. Some (but not all) brands are a good source of vitamin $B_{12.}$
- Seitan (also called wheat gluten): a vegetarian replacement for meat, made of protein (gluten) extracted from flour.
- Soybean: a legume that is an excellent,

inexpensive vegan source of protein and iron; soybeans are used to make a number of vegetarian and vegan substitutions for meat, dairy and eggs.

- Veggie cheese: a cheese-like product often made from soybeans or nuts. These cheeses come in most of the same varieties as dairy cheeses, such as parmesan, mozzarella, and cheddar. However, some soy cheeses are not vegan, as they contain the animal protein casein.
- Plant-based milk: a milk-like product made from plant proteins. Examples include soy, almond, hemp, coconut, and rice milks.
- Tempeh: a replacement for meat, made from fermented soybeans
- Textured vegetable protein: derived from soy flour; TVP is commonly used in vegetarian restaurants as a substitute for ground beef.
- Tofu: a replacement for meat, eggs and cheese, made from curdled soymilk and pressed into blocks. Tofu can be eaten fresh or cooked in many different ways and is an excellent source of protein.
  Types and uses of tofu:
  o Extra firm tofu: frying, roasting, grilling, or marinating
  o Firm tofu: stir-frying, boiling, or filling
  o Soft tofu: pureeing

o Silken tofu: pureeing, simmering, egg substitution; for use in vegan desserts and smoothies

How to Select Meat, Poultry, and Seafood

About 95 percent of pesticides in most American diets come from animal products, like meat, fish, and dairy products. Fish, especially, contain cancer-causing chemicals, such as PCBs, DDT, and the heavy metals mercury, arsenic, lead, and cadmium. Nonorganic meat, fowl, and dairy products are full of steroids, antibiotics, and hormones that have been linked to various cancers and other diseases. These chemicals aren't cooked away—they go right into your body and your cells.

And, while the science is not new, the World Health Organization's (WHO) official classification of processed meats as a Group 1 carcinogen is new and making news. In October, 2015, the International Agency for Research on Cancer (IARC), a subsidiary of WHO, gathered 22 scientists from ten countries to evaluate 800 epidemiological studies that investigated the association of cancer with consumption of red meat or processed meat. As reported in *Lancet Oncology*, "Overall, the Working Group classified consumption of processed meat as "carcinogenic to humans" on the basis of sufficient evidence for colorectal cancer. Additionally, a positive association with the consumption of processed meat was found for stomach cancer." Further,

"The Working Group classified consumption of red meat as "probably carcinogenic to humans." In making this evaluation, the Working Group took into consideration all the relevant data, including the substantial epidemiological data showing a positive association between consumption of red meat red meat and colorectal cancer and the strong mechanistic evidence. Consumption of red meat was also positively associated with pancreatic and with prostate cancer."

Meats are associated with a higher rate of food-borne illness because they need to be kept at certain temperatures and cooked at certain temperatures to avoid parasites. The CDC estimates that each year roughly 1 in 6 Americans (or 48 million people) get sick, 128,000 are hospitalized, and 3,000 die of foodborne diseases.

Meat is a significantly more expensive form of protein than beans, legumes, nuts, and seeds, and organic options are even more expensive. The cost of meat will ideally serve as yet another reason for you to move toward a more plant-based diet, but, while I will continue to strongly urge you in this direction, I understand the realities creating behavioral change. Although I *do not* recommend that you eat the foods listed below, this is a book about choices. So, as you practice moving away from animal foods and toward plant foods, here are some guidelines to help you along.

Meat and Poultry

- As much as possible, choose grass-fed meats from animals that are fed organically.
- To select the leanest options, look for "round" or "loin" in the name of cuts of beef and "loin" in the name of cuts of pork—e.g., beef tenderloin, sirloin, eye-round, top round steak, pork tenderloin.
- Beef labeled "select" has the smallest amount of fat between the muscle, followed by "choice" and "prime" cuts.
- The color of meat indicates freshness. Pork should be a grayish pink; beef should be bright red, with no grayish areas.
- Rely on "% lean" designations on labels, rather than on cuts of meat or descriptions like "natural" or "organic." Look for 95 percent lean.
- Opt for the leanest ground beef for meatloaf, casseroles, and other dishes in which draining or blotting is not possible.
- Purchase skinless chicken or remove the skin before eating; half of the calories in chicken are in the skin.

Seafood

The choices we make as consumers drive the seafood marketplace. Given that nearly 75 percent of the world's fisheries are either fully fished or overfished, these issues are more important than ever. Your purchasing power can make a difference by supporting those fisheries and fish farms that are better for the environment. Sustainable seafood means either fished or farmed seafood that can exist over the long term without compromising species' survival or the health of the surrounding ecosystem.

On a trip to the Monterey Bay Aquarium in California in 1998, I became a big fan of Seafood Watch, a program designed to help consumers become advocates for environmentally friendly seafood. According to the Seafood Watch website, species from sustainable capture fisheries:

BEST CHOICES	GOOD ALTERNATIVES	AVOID
Arctic Char (farmed)	Cod: Atlantic (imported)	Chilean Seabass/Toothfish*
Barramundi (US)	Cod: Pacific (US trawl)	Cobia (Asia, Belize)
Bass: Striped (US hook & line, farmed)	Crab (US) & Snow Crab (Canada)	Cod: Atlantic (Canada & US)
Catfish (US)	Flatfish (Canada & US)	Crab: Red King (Russia)
Clams, Mussels, Oysters (farmed)	Grouper: Red (US Gulf of Mexico)*	Lobster: Spiny (Brazil)
Clams, Oysters (US wild)	Herring: Atlantic (US)	Mahi Mahi (imported)
Cobia (US)	Lobster	Marlin: Blue*
Cod: Pacific (US non-trawl)	Mahi Mahi (US)	Marlin: Striped*
Crab: Dungeness & Stone	Monkfish (US)	Orange Roughy*
Halibut: Pacific (US)	Pangasius/Basa/Swai	Salmon (farmed including Atlantic)
Lobster: Spiny (CA, FL & Mexico)	Pollock: Alaska (US)	Sharks*
Sablefish/Black Cod (AK & Canada)	Sablefish (CA, OR & WA wild)	Shrimp (imported)
Salmon (AK)	Salmon (CA, OR & WA wild)	Skates (US Atlantic)
Sardines: Pacific (Canada & US)	Scallops (wild)	Snapper: Red (US)
Scallops (farmed)	Shrimp (Canada & US wild)	Sturgeon, Caviar (wild)
Shrimp: Pink (OR)	Squid	Swordfish (imported)*
Tilapia (Ecuador & US farmed)	Sturgeon, Caviar (US farmed)	Tuna: Albacore*, Bigeye*, Bluefin*,
Trout: Rainbow (US farmed)	Swordfish (US)*	Canned*, Skipjack, Tongol, Yellowfin*
Canned Tuna, Light: Skipjack (troll,	Tilapia (China & Taiwan)	
pole), Yellowfin (US troll, pole)	Tuna: Bigeye (troll, pole &	
Canned Tuna, White: Albacore	US Atlantic longline*)	
(Canada & US troll, pole)	Tuna: Tongol, Yellowfin (troll, pole)	

Support Ocean-Friendly Seafood

Best Choices are well-managed and caught or farmed in ocean-friendly ways.

Good Alternatives are also an option, but be aware that there are concerns with how they're caught or farmed.

Avoid these items for now. They may be overfished, or caught or farmed in ways that harm other wildlife or their habitats.

* Limit consumption due to concerns about mercury content. Visit edf.org/seafoodhealth

Contaminant information provided by: ENVIRONMENTAL DEFENSE FUND

Seafood may appear in more than one column

Why Do Your Seafood Choices Matter?

Worldwide, the demand for seafood is increasing. Yet many populations of the large fish we enjoy eating are over-fished and, in the U.S., we import over 80% of our seafood to meet the demand. Destructive fishing and fish farming practices only add to the problem.

By purchasing fish caught or farmed using environmentally friendly practices, you're supporting healthy, abundant oceans.

You Can Make A Difference

Support ocean-friendly seafood in three easy steps:

1. Purchase seafood from the green list or, if unavailable, the yellow list. Or look for the Marine Stewardship Council blue eco-label in stores and restaurants.

2. When you buy seafood, ask where your seafood comes from and whether it was farmed or wild-caught.

3. Tell your friends about Seafood Watch. The more people that ask for ocean-friendly seafood, the better!

Learn More

In addition to the recommendations on this guide, we have hundreds more available from our scientists.

To see the complete and most up-to-date list visit us:
• Online at **seafoodwatch.org**
• On our free app
• On our mobile site
• Or join us on Facebook or Twitter

Monterey Bay Aquarium

The seafood recommendations in this guide are credited to the Monterey Bay Aquarium Foundation ©2013. All rights reserved. Printed on recycled paper.

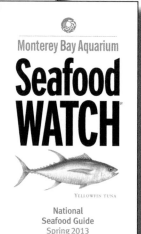

Monterey Bay Aquarium
Seafood WATCH

YELLOWFIN TUNA

National Seafood Guide Spring 2013

- have a low vulnerability to fishing pressure, and hence a low probability of being overfished, because of their inherent life-history characteristics;
- have stock structure and abundance sufficient to maintain or enhance long term fishery productivity;
- are captured using techniques that minimize the catch of unwanted and/or unmarketable species;
- are captured in ways that maintain natural functional relationships among species in the ecosystem, conserve the diversity and productivity of the surrounding ecosystem, and do not result in irreversible ecosystem changes; and
- have a management regime that implements and enforces all local, national, and international laws and utilizes a precautionary approach to ensure the long term productivity of the resource and integrity of the ecosystem.

Below is a picture of the National Seafood Watch Guide. You can download the latest version of the Seafood Watch wallet card for your own region by visiting http://www.mbayaq.org/cr/cr_seafoodwatch/download.asp.

While fish has been touted for its provision of long-chain omega-3 fatty acids, obtaining these healthy fats from fish, even sustainably caught, is not worth the risk of ingesting the toxins and high levels of heavy metals, including mercury, lead, and cadmium, that accumulate in their tissue. This is especially true since the Fukushima Daiichi nuclear disaster in March 2011, which released radioactive material into the air and the Pacific Ocean off Japan. Cesium and other compounds have already been detected in water and species on the West Coast of the United States, along with never-before-seen death and mutations among some species of fish. The devastating impact of these compounds on our environment and food supply is estimated to be up to four times as great as that from Chernobyl.

It is challenging to uncover the truth behind this disaster, given reports that certain authorities are hiding information from the public, but I highly recommend that you educate yourself further so that you can at least be conscious of what has happened. The ramifications of this event have only begun to be revealed. Unfortunately, it is a story in which "time will tell."

How to Select Eggs

Eggs are an animal food. Raising one's own chickens has become a new trend that provides a way to produce eggs without chemicals, but most people are going to purchase their eggs from the store. When you do so:

- Open the egg carton to inspect the eggs and look for uncracked, clean eggs.
- Expect fresh eggs to keep up to four weeks in the refrigerator at forty degrees Fahrenheit.
- Consider refrigerated egg substitutes,

which offer a cholesterol-free option for recipes using eggs.

- Remember that shell color has no effect on an egg's nutritional content and test—the color depends upon the breed of chicken that lays the egg. No breed lays better eggs than another.

How to Select Milk, Yogurt, and Cheese

I grew up loving ice cream and cheese pizza, like most of us, and believed that the protein and calcium content of dairy products was essential to good health. But given all that I have learned about dairy products over the years, and considering that humans were never intended to drink the milk of other mammals, I choose to avoid them and recommend that you do the same.

The best way to support bone health is by eating foods that are alkaline (the opposite of acidic) and rich in bone-supporting nutrients. I have most of the traditional risk factors for osteoporosis—female, white, small body frame, and genetic predisposition. But since I began eating a plant-based diet void of dairy products, my doctor has told me, "Just keep doing whatever it is you're doing," based on my bone scans. For a detailed description of the deception surrounding the dairy industry and its imperative that we consume dairy products to benefit our bones, I suggest you read *Whitewash*, by Joseph Keon.

If and when you consume dairy products, please consider using them sparingly, and choose organic! The pesticides and hormones found in cow's milk may be contributing to some of the health issues we see in children today. For example, it is thought that the hormones in milk may be one reason why girls are maturing at an earlier age than they did a couple of decades ago. When it comes to choosing among whole, 2 percent, 1 percent, and fat-free milk, you should be aware that the only real difference per serving is in the fat and calories. Remember, too, that there are lots of milk alternatives, such as organic soy milk, almond milk, rice milk, hemp milk, coconut milk, hazelnut milk, and oat milk. Plant-based milks are a much better way to grow!

❧

As your awareness about how many natural but limited resources are wasted on inefficient production and shipping of unhealthy food increases, your commitment to sustainable agriculture is likely to grow. Inherently, we know that we are one with the planet. Taking the time to really think about and choose the most sustainable ways to gather food will pay off in terms of nutrition, cost, and personal integrity, too. Good things tend to work together, and this notion is especially true as it pertains to gathering food wisely.

Preparing and Serving Food

NOT ONLY does food give us the opportunity to practice making healthy choices every day, but it also gives us a chance to minister every day. What kind of attitude do we carry with regard to ministering to ourselves with food? What about ministering to others? Do we hastily and grudgingly pack our children's lunch boxes or throw some mac 'n' cheese on the table while shouting for them to come eat lunch? Is making dinner just another task to check off your 'to do' list?

Preparing food with love and intention is not always easy to do, especially when you've got a dozen other things going on and your kids are already hungry, but learning to do so makes all the difference in practicing the Sacred Art of Eating. How can we modify this process for ourselves, for those we serve, and for the sacred? Following are two examples that provide insight and perspective on this subject.

As Jesus and his disciples were on their way, he came to a village where a woman named Martha opened her home to him. She had a sister called Mary, who sat at the Lord's feet listening to what he said. But Martha was distracted by all the preparations that had to be made. She came to him and asked, "Lord, don't you care that my sister has left me to do the work by myself? Tell her to help me!"

"Martha, Martha," the Lord answered, "you are worried and upset about many things, but only one thing is needed. Mary has chosen what is better, and it will not be taken away from her."

—Luke 10:38–42

This biblical passage makes the point that we are often so driven to prepare and serve others in a perfectionist style that we miss out on the more important aspect of enjoying those very acts and sharing companionship with those we serve. Here, Martha is "distracted by all the preparations that had to be made" in order to prepare for Jesus's visit.

Joanna Weaver, in *Having a Mary Heart in a Martha World*, imagines the following about her preparations:

This, she decides, will be a banquet fit for a messiah. For the Messiah. ... Like a military general, she barks commands to her kitchen staff. Soak the lentils! Pound the grain! Knead the dough! So many things to do and so little time. She must make sure the centerpiece and the napkins match, that the servant pours the wine from the right and not the left.

Have you ever felt that way about preparing a meal for someone special? Or when planning a dinner party? Or hosting a family gathering at holiday time? I know I have. How quickly does our lovely intention to prepare something special dissolve into a stressful series of tasks! Jesus rebuked not Martha's *act* of preparing him a meal, but rather her *attitude*. This reminds me of a conversation I had with a pastor in which he said that church members who have volunteered to prepare meals for those in need often end up rushing through the process, complaining along the way. As with Mary, it is not the act of loving service that is the problem; it's allowing that act to irritate and agitate us.

The same message was taught by Catholic monk and author Brother Lawrence, who explains that it's not just *what* we do for Christ that matters but *how* we go about doing it. Lawrence joined a monastery in Paris, expecting to spend his days in prayer and meditation. Rather, he was assigned to the monastery kitchen, full of routine duties and cleaning. Perhaps because of his great distaste for this position, he realized spiritual wisdom that he later shared in his book, *The Practice of the Presence of God*: "The time of business does not with me differ from the time of prayer; and in the noise and clutter of my kitchen, while several persons are at the same time calling for different things, I possess God in as great tranquility as if I were upon my knees before the Blessed Sacrament."

Most of us don't live in a monastery, but many of us can totally relate to the "noise and clutter of the kitchen, while several persons are at the same time calling for different things." How did Brother Lawrence manage his duties with the tranquility and calm nature that characterized him? By practicing the presence of God. I love that he uses the word "practice" in the title of his book. As I've explained already, one of my favorite reasons for looking to food for sacred inspiration and personal growth is that we are dependent upon it for life. As such, it gives us a lifetime of opportunity to *practice* being present. When we prepare food, we can do so in a sacred manner. That is, we can remind ourselves that such an act is ultimately intended to nourish the body, mind, and spirit, as well as provide communion with others.

What to Prepare

Part of setting the table is deciding what food to serve. For those serving children, it is the parent's responsibility to offer something nutritious and appetizing, since kids are generally not capable of preparing their own food. We have discussed at length what foods comprise a healthy meal, but another issue is serving everyone around the table the same foods. In other words, don't be a short-order cook. Preparing a beautiful rice-based dish for your husband, macaroni and cheese for your daughter, and a peanut butter and jelly sandwich for your son not only requires a lot of extra food preparation but does little to encourage healthy eating habits or a shared experience. Children who get whatever they ask for are likely to ask for the same thing over and over again. It is not uncommon for such kids to subsist on two or three primary meals, such as pasta, pizza, and hot dogs. If you don't have to provide each person around the table with exactly what he or she wants, you have the chance to give all of them a variety of more nutritious foods while saving yourself the time of making different meals for everyone.

Try making a list of the foods you and your family like, and create your meals around those. Then make a commitment to incorporating one new food into your diet every week. Choose one that you do not hate, and add it sparingly to a dish that includes other foods. For example, if you dislike brussels sprouts, don't choose that food. If you are not crazy about asparagus but don't mind it, add some chopped asparagus to a vegetable soup. You'll probably still like the soup, and if you continue to do this, you'll gradually expand your repertoire of choices.

Anything you prepare can become a sacred art, but the more you choose to prepare vegan meals, the more closely you will align yourself with the Sacred Art of Eating. Practice will make doing so second nature. Excepting the obvious ham and eggs or steak and potatoes, many foods you might consider eating today can be prepared in vegan fashion. If you are Imperfectly Vegan, most of your recipes will be vegan. As such, the following guidelines are congruent with eating vegan, allowing for those occasional dishes or dining out experiences in which you eat small amounts of animal foods.

- Eat plant-based meals. This, of course, is the easiest thing to do. When you decide to remove animals from your diet, you will discover a new world of plant-based dishes, such as lentil soup, coconut curry vegetable dishes, and sweet potato fries.

- Omit animal-based ingredients. When cooking vegan, you have the option of simply omitting any meat, fish, cheese, or other animal-based ingredient from the dish. Make burritos without meat, cheese, and sour cream, for example. Load up instead with rice, black and pinto beans, lettuce, salsa, sautéed veggies and guacamole. Simple, satisfying, and delicious!

- Offer animal-based ingredients on the side, so that people have the opportunity to choose for themselves whether or not to consume those ingredients. Once people know you're Imperfectly Vegan, they will help you to be so. For example, when my friend Kim made a beautiful salad of greens, quinoa, and beets, she left the blue cheese off mine and made it available on the side for those who wanted it. That simple step alone makes a statement that eating animal foods is a choice.

- Substitute animal foods with plant-based analogues. This is another easy trick that is easy to implement once you are aware of the products. For example, substitute cow's milk with almost any plant-based milk, including coconut, rice, almond, oat, hemp, and soy milk. Condiments like mayonnaise can be replaced with vegan mayonnaise, and sour cream with vegan sour cream. Some stores even sell vegan gravy. And for those who are ready to adopt a plant-based diet but really don't want to give up the feeling of eating meat, there are lots of vegan sausages, salami, hot dogs, burgers, bacon, lunch meats, pulled pork, ground beef, and more. These can be eaten alone (as hot dogs and burgers) or used in recipes (like vegan chili using faux ground beef). Personally, I don't even care to pretend that I'm eating meat and so don't buy these items regularly, but they do provide a nice alternative to those transitioning into an Imperfectly Vegan lifestyle. Just be sure to buy

Other easy substitutions include the following:

SUBSTITUTE THIS:	WITH THIS:
chicken broth	vegetable broth or "no-chicken" chicken broth
beef broth	mushroom broth
cow's milk	soy, almond, oat, hemp, rice, coconut milk
butter	margarine or coconut oil
parmesan cheese	nutritional yeast
anchovies	dried seaweed
creamer	organic soy creamer
meat	baked tofu, vegan varieties
egg	1 tablespoons ground flax seed + 3 tablespoons water
bacon	"veggie" bacon
mayonnaise	vegan mayonnaise
sour cream	vegan sour cream
salami, sausage, turkey, etc.	vegan meats

organic or non-GMO varieties, since many are made with soy or corn, two crops that tend to be genetically modified.

- Modify a recipe by substituting plant-based ingredients for animal-based ingredients. Once you get the hang of it, this is actually quite easy to do. For example, *The Silver Palate Cookbook* has a Mediterranean chicken salad recipe that calls for cooking chicken breasts in water, along with some vegetables and spices, and then tearing the chicken into pieces. The chicken is then combined in a large bowl with Niçoise olives, capers, cherry tomatoes, green beans, olive oil, lemon juice, oregano, and salt and pepper to taste, and served over couscous. Well, I simply pass on cooking and shredding the chicken and use garbanzo beans instead. Not only is it faster and easier to prepare, but it also costs less and loses nothing in terms of flavor. I have served this at many gatherings, and someone always ends up asking me for the recipe.

- Gather vegan recipes. The growing vegan movement means such dishes are easier than ever to find. A Google search for "vegan cookbooks" on May 19, 2014, yielded 4,760,000 results, and a search for "vegan recipes" brought up 82,400,000 results. Online videos are especially nice for demonstrating how to prepare less familiar dishes and items, like homemade almond milk, for example. (You'll find a list of recommended vegan cookbooks and cooking blogs in this book's Resources section.)

- Many vegan recipes are simply plant-based versions of more familiar recipes. For example, vegan butternut squash soup is made using coconut milk and vegetable broth instead of cow's milk and chicken broth, respectively. Vegan blueberry muffins can be made using coconut milk instead of cow's milk, coconut oil instead of butter, and ground flax and water instead of an egg.

Imperfectly Vegan Cooking Methods

In addition to helping you control fat and calories, cooking at home offers the best possible opportunity to monitor how much of each of those elements your food will contain and allows you to control the freshness and quality of raw ingredients. Fresh plant foods are easiest, and usually most nutritious, eaten raw, but there is not enough evidence to prioritize a raw food diet over one that includes some cooked foods. Easy ways to add raw foods to your diet on a daily basis include snacking on raw fruits, vegetables, and nuts, eating green salads, and drinking plant-based, whole food smoothies. And while it is recommended that we eat some raw foods every day, most of us will want to cook some of our food, as cooking lends itself to a wider variety of culinary possibilities and, moreover, can actually increase the availability of some compounds. For example, the lycopene content of a tomato becomes more available when the tomato is cooked, which is why tomato sauce offers more of this benefit than a raw tomato does.

Cooking vegan is not that different from any other type of cooking. As with all cooking, the method you use to prepare vegan dishes can make a big difference in their nutritional content, particularly in regard to fat and calories. Fresh produce should not be cooked until it is limp and tasteless. Cook it "crisp-tender" by steaming or grilling your veggies, instead of boiling, for example. When you boil vegetables, water soluble nutrients leave the food and stay in the water. That's why cooking veggies in soups is a good method for retaining their nutritional contribution. Following are two lists of cooking methods that provide less fat and calories and more fat and calories, respectively:

Cooking Methods That Can Mean Less Fat and Calories:
- Baked
- Barbecued
- Boiled
- Braised
- Broiled
- Grilled
- Poached
- Roasted
- Steamed
- Stewed
- Stir fried

Cooking Methods That Can Mean More Fat and Calories:
- Batter fried
- Deep fried
- Pan fried
- Buttered
- Creamed
- Crispy
- Breaded

Preparing Food with Love and Intention

Now that we know what to prepare, how do we practice presence in the kitchen? First and foremost, we want to learn how to slow down. Slowing down helps us to live in the present. It is here that we can really appreciate the unique attributes of the ingredients we are combining into meals. Having the presence of mind to savor the taste of fresh herbs could make a difference in how much we use. Taking the time to finely chop an onion could prevent us from cutting our finger along with it. Taking time to be sure that you have all the necessary ingredients may save you an unnecessary trip to the store at a potentially crucial step in the cooking process. And slowing down keeps us from getting caught up in too many other distractions. Trying to answer phone calls, respond to e-mail, and fold the laundry at the same time as preparing a meal can quickly become a recipe for disaster.

In the 1980s, an organization called Slow Food was started by an Italian food and wine writer named Carlo Petrini. In 2014, the organization has 150,000 members in 150 countries. Its initial aim was to protest the opening of a McDonald's in the heart of Rome and to promote the preservation of local traditions in the face of the influx of processed food across the globe. The Slow Food movement upholds the firm conviction that people get more out of preparing their own food than from always having strangers prepare it for them. Perhaps the most important reason to slow down is to foster a genuine appreciation for food, which will nourish your relationship with it.

Allowing Creativity to Flow in the Kitchen

When it comes to cooking, we would do well to remember that we are in a cocreative relationship with the earth: the Earth provides the ingredients, and we provide the effort to cook something up. One of the exciting aspects of this cocreation is that we cannot be certain of the result. It is about two forces coming together to create something entirely new.

A fun and easy way to engage in this collaboration is to wing it with the ingredients hiding out in your refrigerator and pantry. This organic and free-form way of preparing food has been inspired in me from two primary sources: renowned Bay Area chef Alice Waters and the Food Network. Alice Waters, pioneer of the locally grown food movement, led the way with the idea of creating a menu based on whatever was available from the garden that day. If the blueberries had reached their peak, blueberry sorbet would likely make an appearance on the menu. If a local farm had just harvested a bunch of dino kale, she'd likely create a salad or soup with it. The inspiration comes from the food itself. What pairs well with this particular ingredient? What other flavors complement it? What other colors or textures help feature its unique qualities?

Contestants on the Food Network show *Chopped* are given a basket of four mystery ingredients and then asked to use them in an appetizer, main course, or dessert. Watching this series inspires me to be more experimental in my approach to cooking; it makes me eager to see what I can do with the melon that I served yesterday and need to use up today.

Another fun way to inspire creativity is to prepare food with others. Involving children in the process may be the best way to ensure your ability to stay present. It is also a great way to encourage them to try new foods. If they help prepare it, they are much more likely to eat it. Lynda Rextroat, Founder of The Cooking with Kids Foundation, a non-profit serving the East Bay Area, understands this quite well and thus provides educational classes that inspire kids to cook up fresh ingredients. Can a child like radishes, beets, and cauliflower? You bet! Cooking alongside friends can be very fulfilling as well. Since 1994, my husband and I have celebrated New Year's Eve by participating with other couples in what we call a Dining Extravaganza. Basically, each couple chooses a menu item (appetizer, soup, salad, main course, side dish, or dessert), brings their own ingredients to the hosting house, and prepares the item in the kitchen just before serving. Needless to say, we end up eating all night long! And while we always enjoy the food and increasingly rambunctious conversation, it is the time in the kitchen that we remember most. Finally, it is fun and time- and cost-efficient to gather with friends or neighbors to cook large batches of food that everyone can then split and take home to both eat that week and/or freeze for later.

Sometimes when you allow your creativity to flow, you will make the most exquisite additions to a meal at the last moment. One of my favorite firsthand experiences with this possibility happened when I was hosting my two-year-old's playgroup on Halloween in 1998. I had all of the usual foods to serve: bagels and cream cheese, fresh fruit (cantaloupe, blueberries, and bananas), cookies, decaffeinated and regular coffee, hot apple cider, and so on. After everything had been arranged, I had a flash of creative insight. I ended up making black and orange signs for each of the foods. As if wearing a costume themselves, the foods transformed into "boogels and scream cheese," "cadaverloupe, booberries, and boonanas," "not-so-spooky cookies," "decapitated and jugular coffee," and "hot apple spider." Of course, the foods themselves stayed the same, but the creativity came through in how it was served—and I have been replicating that cast of characters ever since (with a few plant-based alternatives to the original items).

Serving Food with Love and Intention

Along with knowing *what* to prepare, knowing *how* to serve food is also important in creating an environment that supports the Sacred Art of Eating. Key components include how we set the table and how we present the food.

How we set the table makes a statement about how much we value the dining experience. To create

an atmosphere that invites your family or guests to really take pleasure in their meal and its ambience, consider setting the table with flowers or candles. They don't have to be fancy or cost a lot to foster the idea that the dining experience is about more than eating. It is about enjoying time together and positive conversation. For many families, mealtime is the only time when everyone gathers as a group. As such, it is worthwhile to take a bit of extra time to

make it meaningful. To foster integrity between how we eat and how we care for the planet, you might also consider using eco-friendly serving dishes and utensils. For example, use porcelain plates, cups, and utensils, instead of disposable ones; use cloth towels and napkins, instead of paper ones; and use reusable glass or metal containers, instead of plastic storage bags.

Several practical steps in regard to how food is presented can make a significant difference in fostering positive eating habits. For one thing, it is generally best to keep serving dishes off the table in order to help regulate hunger and satiety. Studies show that people will eat the amount of food that is put in front of them. One experiment, for example, involved comparing two groups: one had a soup bowl filled with soup; the other had a soup bowl that provided an endless supply of soup. In other words, as the second group ate from the soup bowl, it would continue to fill up. The researchers found that the group with the endless soup bowl continued to eat the soup until it eventually stopped filling up, thereby consuming more calories. When the visual cue of food is on the table right in front of people, it is very easy to take more even when hunger has been satisfied. So, rather than putting the entire casserole dish on the table, distribute one serving to each person and keep the large dish on the counter or stove. That way, your guest can better determine whether or not he really needs more food.

Along these same lines, it is also a good practice to serve up less, rather than more, food. Because, again, people are likely to eat what is put in front of them, if you serve someone a small muffin, that's what she'll eat. If you serve her a large muffin, that's what she'll eat. It's much better to serve less and then let people ask for more if that's what they want.

To encourage a diverse palate among children, it's important to offer at least a couple of foods that you *know* they like, along with the new food. This takes some of the focus and pressure off kids to try the new food. If all they see on their plate is one new food item, even if it is the main course, chances are, they will shut down. Offering something that is familiar and liked allows them to enjoy their meal while encouraging their adventurous spirit.

❧

Too often, preparing and serving food feels like work. But it doesn't have to be that way. The trick to turning kitchen duty into a sacred art begins by slowing down. Once we can do that, everything else falls into place, including a sincere appreciation for the ingredients. Whether we are following a recipe or using sacred inspiration to create something new, food preparation is an example of how the means can be as important as the end. Serving food is honorable, and doing so in a way that supports healthy eating habits underscores its value. Together, preparing and serving food with love and intention sets the table for a truly nourishing dining experience.

Dining Together

THE FOOD is prepared. The table is set. The dinner bell sounds. It's time to gather with family and friends for a meal.

Sharing a meal is so important that Greeks acknowledge that someone is a friend by saying, "We have shared bread together." This act may celebrate a special occasion or no occasion at all. It may even be a form of romance. It is often said, for example, that "the way to a man's heart is through his stomach." Indeed, food plays an important role in the mating process. Traditionally, women have made men feel nurtured and happy by making them meals. But nowadays the romance of cooking and picnics goes both ways. Many couples enjoy making meals together for each other and for their friends. The foodie movement is rife with tales of spouses who fell in love over their favorite meals.

In Anita Diamant's passionate novel, *The Red Tent*, Leah describes to her daughter, Dinah, her efforts to capture the heart of Jacob:

Leah remembered every bite. "He dipped into the stew over and over again, and had three helpings of bread. I saw that he liked sweets, and that he preferred the honeyed brew to the bitter-flavored drink that Laban gulped down. I knew how to please his mouth, I thought. I will know how to please the rest of him."

I'd like to share with you a sweet and simple story about how food serves as a metaphor for love. When courting my husband during the early days of our relationship, I headed off to Andronico's market on Shattuck Avenue in Berkeley and loaded up my shopping cart with about ten bunches of bananas. When in college, my husband discovered that bananas were a fast, convenient form of good nutrition that filled him up. Ever since then, he has eaten about four bananas a day.

As I unloaded the fruit onto the checkout counter at the market, an old woman behind me said, "Are you planning to make a lot of banana bread?"

I said, "No. I'm trying to tell someone that I love him a whole *bunch*. Do you think it will work?"

She laughed and said, "Well, I don't know, honey, but it sure is good to know that romance is alive and well in Berkeley, California!"

Beyond romance, meals provide quality time and are a practice that encourages healthful bonds, particularly within families. Unfortunately, sitting down to dinner is a concept that many American families can't seem to relate to anymore. With more parents working and children busy with after-school activities, finding time to enjoy meals together seems to be more and more difficult these days. Nonetheless, research continues to demonstrate that family meals promote healthy eating habits. The National Longitudinal Study of Adolescent Health found that teenagers consume more nutritious foods if they eat an evening meal with their parents. In addition, adolescents who eat more than three evening meals per week are significantly less likely to skip breakfast than those who eat fewer family meals. Another study showed that adolescents who eat with their families grow up to be healthier adults who eat more fruit and dark green and orange vegetables and consume fewer soft drinks. Frequency of family meals is also associated with girls eating breakfast as adults, and it is well established that eating breakfast supports weight loss and long-term maintenance. Beyond the nutrition benefits, young people who spend more time eating and talking with their families are also more likely to do well in school and less likely to use drugs, alcohol, and tobacco and to develop eating disorders.

As the mother of two teenagers, I can attest to the truth of the familiar statement "They grow up so fast!" My sons' schedules are so busy that time around the table is often the only opportunity my husband and I have to hear about what our children did that day. If you have kids of your own, treasure these moments before they are gone. Finding time to enjoy a family meal, no matter how simple it might be, can help all families eat well and stay connected.

Expressing Gratitude for Our Food

However you experience the sacred, offering gratitude for the gifts you have been given is one of the most effective ways to nurture your connection to it. Indeed, the universe has gifted us with a bountiful supply of beautiful food. By offering gratitude for our food, we are acknowledging that it did not just appear out of thin air but was produced from the earth and the people who planted, nurtured, and harvested it. And while I certainly don't want to encourage the common parental saying "You'd better eat everything on your plate, because there are people starving in the world," it is important to remember that, indeed, many people in the world are hungry. Holding a bowl of rice or a piece of bread reminds us that there are some who have no food to eat and are without friends or family. Offering gratitude for our food cultivates seeds of compassion that will strengthen us to do something to nourish those who hunger—things like providing surplus harvest to a local food bank or volunteering to serve meals at a homeless shelter in our community. It also helps us to pause long enough to recall the reasons why we value food:

- It tastes good.
- It nourishes our body.
- It gives us energy to do our work.
- It delights our senses.
- It provides a way for us to connect with our family and friends.

There are many ways to give thanks for our food. Any sincere expression of gratitude will serve the same purpose, which is to slow us down enough to connect with the sacred. This alone brings tremendous benefits to our body, mind, and spirit and is one of the many reasons why I so appreciate the relationship between food and spirituality. Given that most of us eat several times or more each day, food serves as one of the most powerful reminders of what we are: divine.

Most cultures and religions have a way to express thanks for what is about to be eaten. Holding a deep connection to the earth, Native Americans honor the exchange of life in regard to food. They ask the Spirit that dwells in the living food—whether animal or plant—for permission to take its life. They then give thanks to the Spirit for its willingness to sacrifice its own life for their benefit and sometimes make an offering of corn or tobacco, for example, in compensation for this sacrifice. Such an act acknowledges that something has been given and received on both sides. Buddhists say a prayer of awareness and gratitude to the interconnected power behind all of life before they begin eating. There is even a tradition in Buddhism of leaving something to eat, such as an orange or other fruit, on an altar in one's home or in a Buddhist temple as a symbolic gift to those who have passed away and to the force within all of life.

Anyone who eats the food that has been prepared for him or her can be equally present to this exchange of life. One of the most common ways to offer gratitude is by saying grace, which is actually a specific form of ritual. One may choose to speak freely from the heart as an individual—even when dining alone—or on behalf of a group. In my family, my mother, whom we call Moma, leads us in a heartfelt prayer at our family gatherings just before we eat. About thirty of us stand in a large circle,

remind us of our intimate connection with food. And while I encourage poetic works as beautiful expressions of gratitude, I also greatly appreciate this reminder from German theologian and mystic, Meister Eckhart: "If the only prayer you say in your whole life is 'thank you,' that would suffice."

If you are not comfortable saying a prayer out loud or do not follow a particular belief system, you can still practice gratitude through silence. If the expression is sincere, the offering will be effective. Silence doesn't just happen; it has to be allowed. It requires us to make a conscious decision not only to refrain from speech, but also to withdraw from activities that fill our minds with noise, such as watching television, listening to the radio, or reading a book. Even in prayer, which people most often do silently, we can be so busy voicing our praise and requests to the sacred that we often don't allow for the space to receive the gifts and messages that the universe intends for us. As with saying grace, a moment of silence can be shared by a group of people or practiced by an individual. The important thing is that this moment be used to consciously appreciate the food about to be eaten.

usually in the kitchen, holding hands. Some of our family members are Christian, some Buddhist, some pagan, and some atheist. In this shared circle, our appreciation for each other and the food that is served unifies us more deeply.

Other people choose to recite or read a specific prayer from their spiritual tradition or from literature. I am especially fond of Kahlil Gibran's *The Prophet* as a source of inspiration for words that

Eating Slowly

There's no doubt about it—we want things fast. All of our technological advances seem to have translated into our having more to do than ever, even though there are still only twenty-four hours in a day. Unfortunately, our societal relationship with food is highly symbolic of our culture's need for speed: Microwave meals in five minutes or less! Lose ten pounds in a week! If you don't get your food within three minutes, your next meal is free! For many, grabbing a meal on the go is a daily practice.

But food offers equal opportunity to slow down. Meals are meant to be enjoyed, rather than simply swallowed. Part of the enjoyment of eating lies in seeing what's on your plate, smelling the food, and taking time to enjoy the process. In many countries, a meal often lasts several hours. In fact, one of Greece's national dietary guidelines is to "eat slowly, preferably at regular times of the day, and in a pleasant environment."

This is called mindful eating. Mindful eating involves taking time to savor all aspects of food, as well as the act of eating. A traditional Japanese tea ceremony, for example, includes a role for each of the senses—watching and listening as the tea pours from pot to cup, picking  up the cup and feeling the heat, smelling the freshly steeped herbs, and, lastly, tasting the brew. Mindful eating can cultivate seeds of compassion and understanding that will strengthen us to be more present in the world. We do not need to go to a temple or a church in order to practice this concept. Because our bodies house the sacred, we can practice presence right at the dinner table.

The ritual of the Eucharist is one practice of mindfulness. When Jesus broke the bread and shared it with his disciples, he said, "Eat this. This is my flesh." Buddhist monk Thich Nhat Hanh says, "Jesus knew that if his disciples would eat one piece of bread in mindfulness, they would have real life. In their daily lives, they may have eaten bread in forgetfulness, so the bread was not bread at all."

This simple act of silence may play an even deeper role in regard to our relationship with food, since it is considered a key in breaking addiction. 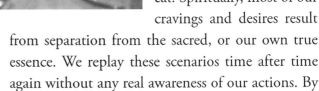 The unconscious habit of reaching for food when we are not hungry is a method for keeping ourselves distracted—from facing our fears or dealing with our emotions. From early childhood, we develop grooves in regard to how we eat. Spiritually, most of our cravings and desires result from separation from the sacred, or our own true essence. We replay these scenarios time after time again without any real awareness of our actions. By taking even the smallest moment of silence before reaching for our food, we take the first essential step to breaking the pattern. The Gene Keys says, "If you could look deeply enough into this desire without acting on it, it would actually burn itself out, which is the underlying purpose of meditation." Here again, our relationship with food serves as a spiritual path that can bring us closer to the sacred with each sacred bite.

Feeding the Five Senses

We derive most of our pleasure through our five senses. There is absolutely nothing better than food to satisfy each of those senses. While it can be argued that sex fulfills this role, how many of us have sex every day, let alone three times a day? The abundance of food in our lives is irrefutable; the opportunity for sex, not so much. Further, the colors, tastes, and textures that are available through food are far more vast than those achieved any other way.

Food's ability to feed our physical senses is a fundamental principle that has gone highly unrecognized but has tremendous potential to alter our attitude toward food. Unfortunately, our technological society has numbed our senses. Sitting in front of our computers all day does little to feed our senses, aside from seeing words pop up on the screen, the feeling of our fingertips on the keyboard, and the clicking in our ears. Why is it that when we go to the movies we have to have something to munch on? Because the movie feeds only our senses of sight and sound (we see and hear the movie). Our senses of touch, taste, and smell still hunger.

What do we do to remedy this situation? Eat popcorn! This is why television viewing and obesity are so closely correlated (as well as the fact that couch potatoes aren't moving their muscles except to blink their eyes and maintain a heartbeat). By getting that bucket of popcorn, we now have something that can satisfy all of our senses.

Let's use an apple to explore the fact that food literally feeds our five senses better than anything else. Following is an exercise that both children and adults can try:

Take an apple and place it in front of you.

Look at the apple with your eyes. What color is it? Is it red, green, or yellow? Is it dirty? Is it shiny?

Touch the apple with your hands. How does it feel? Is it firm or soft? Is it cold or room temperature?

Smell the apple with your nose. Does it have a sweet scent?

Hear the apple crunch as you bite into it. What sounds do you hear? Skin breaking? Chewing? Juices being released?

Taste the apple with your mouth (your tongue and taste buds). How does it taste? Sweet? Tart? Other?

Digestion

Perhaps surprisingly, digestion begins before we even put food into our mouth. That's because when we see, touch, smell, or hear about food, our salivary glands begin to secrete enzymes that will further the digestive process. We then chew on the food to begin breaking it down into smaller pieces that the body can more easily handle. This is an area where it is really important to slow down. It is not uncommon for people to chow down a meal within minutes. Eating too fast leads to poor communication between the stomach and the brain and to incomplete digestion of food. It's important to chew food well enough to facilitate absorption of the nutrients and to avoid constipation. Can you imagine the poor intestinal wall facing huge particles of food that have not been chewed and broken down very well? Yikes! Remember, we are in a cocreative relationship with our bodies—that means we need to make sure we do our part and don't just expect our bodies to handle everything with magical ease.

Dessert

Life wouldn't be complete without dessert, would it? A human preference for sweet taste is innate, and sweeteners can increase the pleasure of eating. Dessert is that moment at the end of a meal when your host or server asks if you want something sweet and you look around at your fellow diners as if to say, *I will if you will.* Most of us weigh the pros and cons and feel peer pressure to share a dessert sometimes. Is it a special enough occasion? Are you full from the meal you just ate? Are you feeling strong and able to resist temptation? Will you be able to enjoy it without feeling as if there is a price to pay afterward?

These are good questions to ask yourself, given that approximately 13 percent of adults' total caloric intake came from added sugars between 2005 and 2010. Among adults, however, one-third of calories from added sugars came from beverages, and in children and adolescents, 40 percent of calories from added sugars came from beverages. Thus, moving away from sodas and other sugar-laden beverages is the most significant step in reducing sugar intake for most people, much more than eliminating dessert.

One of the world's most beloved dessert foods is chocolate, which more than a billion people consume each day. It is made from the beans of the cacao tree, whose botanical name is *Theobroma*, which aptly means "food for the gods." I may be a nutrition expert, but remember that I was also born to a father who worked for See's Candies throughout my childhood and well into my adulthood, so I know well the delicious delights of sweets and the happiness you can bring to loved ones when sharing

or serving something rich and sugary. We need good nutrition, but life is a balancing act and is best when it's enjoyed, so dessert shouldn't be forbidden altogether (though it is best reserved for special occasions). And keep in mind that many cultures find fresh fruit, the sweetest treat of all, to be the perfect end to a meal. Understand the upsides and downsides, and allow yourself some sweet pleasure.

From appetizers to dessert, food is most enjoyed when shared with others. Beyond nourishing the physical body, dining with others nourishes our connections. Whether we're in a restaurant or a school cafeteria or at a picnic, a ballpark, a wedding, or our own dining table, the fact that we all need to eat reminds us of our shared humanness. Taking the time to consciously express gratitude for the food that keeps us alive and so thoroughly feeds our five senses is a practice worth developing. Whether by reading a piece of scripture or literature, by speaking heartfelt words, or by taking a moment of silence, we'll find that appreciation for the planet and people that made our food available will increase our integrity around it. And learning to eat slowly will not only foster better digestion but also further our ability to appreciate the food we eat.

As you dine with others, I encourage you to model healthier food choices and eating behaviors. They are contagious and of great benefit to all.

CHAPTER TEN

Cleaning Up the Kitchen

NOW WE SIT, well satisfied, all of our senses delighted. As we continue making conversation, our body is working to digest the food we've eaten. Imagine a rope—twenty-five-feet long—amazingly, that represents the length of the average intestinal tract. Digestion time varies between individuals and between men and women but, on average, it can take between twenty-three and thirty hours to move food through your system. It takes about six to eight hours for food to pass

through the stomach and small intestine. It then enters the large intestine (colon) for further digestion, absorption of water, and, finally, elimination of undigested food. This process crudely reminds us that we are constantly undergoing transformation. Truly, we are never the same person twice. At the speed of light, we become something different than what we once were, if even for just having had the experience. And so the question is: In what directions are we transforming?

*Dance the orange. Who can forget it,
drowning in itself, how it struggles through
against its own sweetness.
You have possessed it.
Deliciously it has converted to you.*

Whole plant foods convert us into something much healthier than we would be without them. As we discussed earlier, our health depends first and foremost upon what we eat, among other lifestyle factors. As evidenced by the exciting field of epigenetics, positive behaviors and attitude trump bad genes! The body's natural inclination is to be

Transformation does not imply any sense of "good" or "bad." We are wise not to judge our experiences. As with so many things in life, what we think is a "bad" or negative event may turn out to be the best thing that could have happened to us. Losing a job, for example, may force us to reconsider what we want to do with our time and lead us to something much more supportive of our authentic self. When it comes to how we eat, however, we can confidently state that food either builds us up or breaks us down. In either case, our intimate relationship with food is highlighted by the fact that food actually becomes a part of us. The following poem, by Rainer Maria Rilke, from *Sonnets to Orpheus*, I, 15, illustrates the transformation of food into us:

well. Consider a cut transforming into a scab and then a scar that fades with time, or the regeneration of speech after a stroke. The body does all that it can to heal, even against our lack of support. Remember that cancer, as with all of our disease states, is just a word. Cancer represents damaged cells that mutate and replicate. Given optimal nutrition, such damage can be potentially healed as the body undergoes cellular regeneration. We are not doomed to the same disease states as our ancestors unless we follow the same lifestyle practices they did. The human body has approximately twenty-two thousand genes that have millions of switches that can be turned on and off. These switches respond to our environment, including what we eat. If we choose to take better care of ourselves than our ancestors did, we can expect to live longer with better health.

Catalyzing Change

Symbolically, while we have enjoyed our meal, we have transformed the kitchen into a mess. For me, this brings us full circle in regard to the Sacred Art of Eating. As you may recall, before exploring what and how to eat in ways that nourish us on many levels, we had to take an honest look at our current—and daunting—health conditions. Briefly, populations around the world increasingly suffer from the impact of being overweight and obese, while others hunger for food every day. Children born today are not expected to live longer than

their parents, should current trends continue and preventable disease like heart disease remain the leading causes of death. On an environmental level, we are facing dire conditions that leave the survival of various species, as well as that of the planet, in question. For a more extensive review of the food-related issues that impact our individual, communal, and environmental well-being, please refer to chapter 4.

Continuing to eat in a way that poisons our bodies and the planet is, in simplistic terms, like never cleaning up after a meal, leaving the dishes to pile up for years and years to come. The longer we leave the dirty dishes in the sink, the worse the situation becomes. The good news is that we can turn things around. We can use our free will to participate in cleaning up the mess that we humans have created within ourselves and on the planet. We can begin through our dynamic relationship with food. Food brings home the fact that each of us is a catalyst for change.

Certainly, education and personal responsibility are critical elements of any program aiming to reduce obesity, but they are not sufficient on their own. As the November 2014 McKinsey Global Obesity Report states, existing evidence indicates that no single intervention, and certainly not individual conscious choice alone, is likely to have a significant overall effect. Rather, we need a variety of initiatives that create positive change in the environment and societal norms to reverse the health burden, such as reducing default portion sizes, changing marketing practices, and restructuring urban and education environments to facilitate physical activities. Successful precedents suggest that a combination of top-down corporate and government interventions,

together with bottom-up community-led ones, will be required to change public health outcomes. That said, our greatest power lies within our personal responsibility. Doesn't it make sense that whatever can help heal the world should be something that each one of us can do? We are entering a new age in which the individual *I* is being replaced by the collective *we*. As we mature spiritually, growing to identify with humanity as a whole, we will more naturally consider the impact of our decisions and choose those that serve our greater body.

I can't think of anything more symbolic of our interconnectedness than food. Each and every one of us is absolutely dependent upon it for life. From birth until death, we are in relationship with it. Not one of us can live without it. Food demonstrates

that, at our core, we are more similar to one another than we are different. It is the greatest symbolic manifestation of our oneness: oneness with the sacred, oneness with each other, and oneness with the planet. DreamingBear Baraka Kanaan says, "We are not responsible for the world we've been given, but we are responsible for the world we leave behind." Because we eat food every day, and because our choices make a difference, we all have an *ability to respond* to our current conditions.

Further, because my purpose is to heal and strengthen our relationship with food in order to support our relationship with the sacred, and because we are on the subject of "cleaning up," I would like to briefly discuss the consequences of diet on the pineal gland. Though this concept is not yet proven or understood by Western medicine and is not generally discussed in professional nutrition circles, the pineal gland is very significant among spiritual communities and, as such, I would be remiss not to mention it. In fact, to me, as a shamanic practitioner, it is of primary importance.

The pineal gland, about the size of a pea and shaped like a pinecone, is part of the nervous system. It is located in the brain behind our two eyes (behind the pituitary gland), which is why it is called the "third eye." This gland serves as a gateway between the physical and spiritual realms by releasing a compound called dimethyltryptamine, or DMT. It is most active upon birth and death but can play a leading role in helping us to achieve higher states of consciousness throughout our lives. Indigenous shamanic cultures brew a plant-based medicine, called ayahuasca, to provide this compound for divinatory and healing purposes. Though not to the same degree, we can support its expression on a daily basis through our ability to remember our dreams, achieve altered states of consciousness, and improve our intuition. While research has long supported the benefit of dreams to our health—physically, emotionally, and spiritually—our society, sadly, fails to honor this free and most valuable gift. How often do we make an effort to remember our dreams? How often do we invite our children to share their dreams with us? To not remember and work with our dreams is like being given a gift that we never open.

While the pineal gland's resurgence in discussion has only recently begun, it has been recognized throughout many spiritual traditions, including Christianity, Buddhism, and Hinduism. Consider that the Buddha's head is covered with small pinecone shapes and that Buddhists often wear a dot on their forehead to mark the third eye, or "seat of the soul." So, what does food have to do with the pineal gland? Well, our highly processed, fast-food lifestyle leads to calcification of the pineal gland, which essentially shuts it down. One of the worst offenders of this type of calcification is fluoride, which is found in tap water and most toothpastes.

Other toxins thought to calcify the pineal gland include tobacco, alcohol, meat, processed foods, and chemically sprayed fruits and vegetables. Children have the best opportunity to protect the pineal gland when they are fed a whole-food, plant-based diet. For those of us who have subsisted on a more toxic diet, we are well advised to detoxify this gland as much as possible. Becoming Imperfectly Vegan, as well as avoiding tobacco and excessive alcohol, and including regular meditation, yoga, and exercise will all help to revitalize this spiritual gateway.

This underscores once again the fact that we are in a cocreative relationship with the sacred. We are spiritual beings born into human bodies that serve us beyond our understanding. What we choose to do with them and how we choose to care for them is our choice, because we have been gifted with free will. A deeper spiritual life is available to every one of us and how we eat is foundational to that process.

One Last Reminder: Be Imperfectly Vegan

While we have to eat in order to live, *what* and *how* we eat is, indeed, a voluntary act. What causes someone to shift toward a vegetarian diet? The reasons vary even among the same people over time. The *Vegetarian Times*'s 2008 "Vegetarianism in America" study indicated that over half of current vegetarians eat a vegetarian diet to improve their overall health, with specific references to weight loss, weight maintenance, and "natural approaches to wellness." Over half cited animal welfare, nearly half cited environmental concerns, and about one-third cited food safety concerns. Clearly, people often have multiple reasons for being vegetarian that may change with understanding or new conditions.

In 2011, a Harris Interactive Service Bureau survey showed almost sixteen million Americans to be vegetarian, about half of those vegan. Additionally, in a previous study, more than twenty-two million people said they largely follow a vegetarian-inclined diet, and nearly twelve million more expressed interest in transitioning to vegetarianism in the future. Is it any surprise, then, that news outlets declared 2014 the "year of the vegan" on both sides of the Atlantic? I'd say we're seeing a strong trend toward being Imperfectly Vegan!

Overall, being Imperfectly Vegan is an approach to eating that focuses on eating plants: nuts, seeds, grains, fruits, and vegetables. While represented by just a few words, these categories represent thousands of specific foods and an infinite array of dishes that can be prepared using them. As the 2013 International Conference on Vegetarian Nutrition concluded, one of the most consistent findings of nutritional epidemiology is that plant centered diets have more favorable chronic disease outcomes. The inclusion of colorful fruits and vegetables rich in plant nutrients is key! There is also a strong emphasis on reducing or eliminating animal foods from the diet because their production places such a heavy burden on our health, as well as being cruel to animals and negatively impacting the environment. Given our increasing intake of meat consumption alongside inadequate intakes of produce, we still have much room for improvement—but I see that as good news, because it offers us the opportunity to transform our personal relationship with food for the betterment of all.

The reason I developed the term "Imperfectly Vegan" is that it keeps the focus on following a whole-food, plant-based diet while at the same time allowing for realistic evolution. Even *I* am intimidated by the idea of being vegan—the word feels so absolute. In reality, even the most dedicated vegan will falter at times, but that shouldn't be a reason to give up on being vegan altogether; rather, it can simply represent an opportunity to acknowledge our humanness.

A colleague of mine asked our vegetarian group, "How many of you have inadvertently eaten animal products?" She then shared that she had done so, accidentally mistaking a real meatball for the veggie ones offered at a baby shower. When she tasted and felt the meat in her mouth, she gagged and spit it out. She felt awful and angry at herself. For the committed vegan, such an oversight may lead someone to question whether he or she is a true vegan. Being Imperfectly Vegan allows for human deviation, whether conscious or not. It also allows

people not to be so intimidating to others who are interested in a vegan-based way of eating but not nearly as confident that they can pull it off.

For those who are new to vegetarianism on any level, being Imperfectly Vegan allows for experimentation and provides something to work toward. In other words, if you do not want to give up meat altogether, *don't!* Instead, eat smaller amounts of meat less frequently and choose the highest quality sources whenever possible. You can accomplish this by going meatless for at least one day out of the week and then one week out of the month. Or take it meal by meal, cutting out animal products as much as possible. As you expand your appreciation of what it means to eat in a sacred fashion, you will find it easier and easier to release meat from your diet.

As for the planet, it is not necessary to give up meat completely in order to participate in this type of global healing. Sixty million people could be fed adequately with the grain that would be saved if Americans reduced their meat intake by just 10 percent—in other words, by giving up meat less than one day per week. Of course, I encourage us to go above and beyond this call and I am confident that we can do so as we become more and more enlightened about our relationship with the earth.

The rapidly increasing number of excellent resources available today makes experimenting with vegan recipes easy and delicious. (See this book's Resources section for more information.) Now that 40 percent of the American population is interested in vegetarian options, it's no wonder that Starbucks is beginning to offer almond milk, in addition to organic soy milk, as an alternative to cow's milk, and restaurants are increasingly adding vegan options to their menus. As Margaret Mead said, "Never doubt that a small group of thoughtful, committed people can change the world. Indeed, it is the only thing that ever has."

food that a few minutes of sweet taste matters more than doing right by the planet?

I grew up going to McDonald's. It was the fun, special treat that the marketers had intended. The same was true for my husband. And so, when we had children, there was a part of us that wanted to carry on the McTradition. We didn't go often—rarely, in fact—but then even that became too much for me. I was not living with integrity. And so even if my husband wanted to stop on our road trip to Lake Tahoe, I planned ahead with a snack and left him and our sons to their own McDevices. After doing this several times, they stopped asking to go as well, and in fact, both of my sons now consider most fast-food chains "evil." Their new perspective began when I took a stand for myself. Our actions are noticed. Our actions make a difference.

Eating for Something Greater Than Ourselves

The impact of our individual choices is even greater if we are responsible for what others eat— whether we are parents or grandparents or caretakers or teachers or restaurant owners or supermarket managers or politicians and so on. Look at the role of food in our educational, religious, and business environments. Are we using sugary treats to reward and celebrate special moments? Is our message about

Studies show that serving something other and greater than ourselves—as pregnant women are apt to do—also nourishes us physically, mentally, and spiritually and can drive our behaviors toward better health. To that end, food provides us with a lifetime of opportunities to show compassion with our dietary choices. With regard to our global community, there is nothing more basic and essential than our shared need for food. Eating in ways that help balance the world's food supply is one of the most powerful demonstrations of true love. We can provide the hungry with the food they need if we choose for ourselves healthier foods that use fewer resources. Our society has become sadly desensitized to the origins of food and what it takes to get it to the table. Most of us are unaware that the amount of water needed to make enough meat for one hamburger is equal to the amount of water used in one month by a family of four in the Amazon, or that it takes five to twenty calories of fossil fuel to produce one calorie of food energy in the form of meat. (For more on these topics, refer to chapter 4.) The production of plant food is far more energy efficient.

There are truly enough resources to feed several times the current world population, but as long as a minority demands large quantities of meat, there is going to be a life and death struggle for food somewhere in the world. On an environmental level, according to a November 2014 study in *Nature*, "rising incomes and urbanization are driving a global dietary transition in which traditional diets are replaced by diets higher in refined sugars, refined fats, oils, and meats. By 2050 these dietary trends, if unchecked, would be a major contributor to an estimated 80 percent increase in global agricultural greenhouse gas emissions from food production and to global land clearing. Moreover, these dietary shifts are greatly increasing the incidence of type II diabetes, coronary heart disease, and other chronic non-communicable diseases that lower global life expectancies. If widely adopted, alternative diets that offer substantial health benefits could reduce global agricultural greenhouse gas emissions, reduce land clearing and resultant species extinctions, and help prevent such diet related chronic non-communicable diseases. The implementation of dietary solutions to the tightly linked diet-environment-health trilemma is a global challenge, and opportunity, of great environmental and public health importance."

Consider that for each pound of meat, our fields lose about five pounds of topsoil due to deforestation, overgrazing happens in areas too small to support the animal population, and chemical fertilizers for animal feed crops are overused. Whether animal or plant, foods that are grown and transported using environmentally responsible practices must be supported. Such practices conserve natural resources, minimize the quantity of waste generated, and support the ecological survival of the global food system now and in the future. How will you volunteer to eat today?

☙ Final Thoughts ❧

The Sacred Art of Eating has offered up quite a lot to digest. This is a good time to process the information you have received and to explore whether you can transform it into something new. I imagine that you may feel full and a bit overwhelmed. I know I do. But I also feel a great sense of relief about having said what needs to be said. Sausage in the morning, a turkey sandwich for lunch, and beef fajitas for dinner . . . Mother Nature didn't design the food supply for us to have it this easy! Rather, she offers an abundance of beautiful, viable plants for our enjoyment, of which we are not taking full advantage. It's time to honor Mother Nature by cocreating the bodies and the world we live in.

The time and energy you have spent with me on this journey are highly valuable. We can change the world by honoring our personal relationship with food. The fact that we are dependent upon food for life gives us a lifetime of opportunities to practice eating well. Gifted with free will, we have options. I can write this book, or not. You can read it, or not. We can plunder the earth's natural resources in order to feed our cravings, or we can choose to adopt environmentally sustainable eating practices. As we raise our collective consciousness in regard to being Imperfectly Vegan, we will absolutely benefit our individual, communal, and environmental well-being.

Ideally, I have helped to motivate you to adopt better eating behaviors in order to benefit your own quality of life, including by having more energy, improved physical fitness, better sleep, clear skin, and strong hair and nails. But if that isn't enough, perhaps you can reflect upon our meditation of being pregnant with the earth as a reminder to serve something greater than yourself—that is, your local and global communities and the planet itself. In a spiritual sense, there will come a day when we no longer hunger for anything. But until that day comes, our decisions about what to eat can reflect love and compassion toward the collective. Each of us is like one of those unique puzzle pieces that synergistically complete the puzzle.

Certainly, there is paradox in the fact that a properly nourished seed grows into a living plant that is harvested and then, when eaten, dies and gives us life. Our changing seasons provide a time to grieve, mourn, and release what is dying. It is also a special time to invite, welcome, and celebrate what is arising or waiting to be born. It is my sincere intention and desire that *The Sacred Art of Eating* will bring forth a new season for you.

Food for thought

Chapter 1: The Invitation

1. Have you fully considered that you have control over what you eat?

2. How often do you eat when you are not hungry? Why do you do this?

3. How often do you *not* eat even when you are hungry? Why do you do this?

4. How often do you eat something that you don't really like because you don't want to hurt someone's feelings?

5. How often do you stop at a fast-food restaurant because it seems to be the only available option on a road trip?

6. Are you really owning the fact that you are the one who gets to decide what you eat?

7. When you eat unhealthy foods, do you own the fact that you made the decision to do so?

8. Do you consider the consequences to yourself when you eat something?

9. Do you consider the impact on others when you eat something? On animals? On the planet?

Food for Thought

Chapter 2: The Guest List

1. Do you think of yourself as being in a relationship with food?

   - Is this a new idea for you?

   - How does it make you feel to think of yourself in a lifelong relationship with food? Tired? Excited? Hopeful? Anxious? Interested? Hungry? Full? All of the above? Something else?

2. How would you describe your relationship with food:

   - Juicy? Tasty? Delicious?

   - Burdensome? Troublesome? Costly?

   - Evolving? Codependent? Nourishing? Simple? Complex?

   - Like a dear friend that is always there when you need him or her?

   - Like a marriage that has its ups and downs but that you are in until the end?

   - Like an annoying pest that you wish would go away but never does?

   - Like a gift to be enjoyed every day?

   - Like a breath of fresh air—something wonderful but taken for granted?

   - What else?

Have fun with this; try to accept the first thoughts that come to mind without judging them. You may even choose to draw a picture or write a poem about your relationship with food.

3. Do you have difficulty accepting and acknowledging your inner beauty? Why does it seem difficult to do so?

4. What are some ways in which you display your inner beauty to others and the world?

5. Reflect on your beauty through the eyes of someone who loves you. What do you see? If you are a parent, it may help to think about how you see your child. Reflect on your sacred beauty.

6. Pay attention to the things you experience today. Look for the beauty in those things. What do you see?

7. Write a new definition of beauty. Draw a picture, write a poem, or sing about it.

8. Can you think of some reasons to give up dieting?

9. What diet plans have you followed in the past?

10. Did you lose weight as a result? If so, were you able to maintain the weight loss, or did you gain the weight back, and perhaps even more?

11. What did you like about the plans? What didn't you like?

12. Did the diets help you to adopt new and improved eating behaviors?

13. Are you open to adopting a new approach to eating?

Food for Thought

Chapter 3: Your Hostess

1. Have you tried to control factors in your life that really are not within your control?

2. Have you ever felt as if you were the only one who experienced something? Have you ever had a problem that didn't seem to have a name?

3. What factors in your life do you *have* control over?

4. What factors in your life do you *not have* control over?

Food for thought

Chapter 4: Eating for Our Individual, Communal, and Environmental Well-Being

Individual Well-Being

1. Are you experiencing poor health? What health issues are you experiencing? How are they impacting your everyday life?
2. Are you open to changing the way you eat to reduce your risk of illness and disease?
3. What is the worst thing that could happen if you changed the way you eat now?
4. What is the best thing that could happen if you changed the way you eat now?

Communal Well-Being

1. Have you considered that the way you eat impacts the health of others? For example, if you are a parent, do you accept that the foods you purchase, serve, and eat impact your child's relationship with food?
2. Do you eat animal foods? Do you consider how the animal was raised and treated before consuming it? Why or why not?
3. Would you be willing to make some personal changes if they would support others to be healthier? Why or why not?

Environmental Well-Being

1. Have you accepted that the planet is experiencing a health crisis? Why or why not?
2. Do you accept that the way we eat impacts the environment? How does that make you feel?
3. Are you aware that the planet's poor health is impacting our food supply? How does that make you feel?
4. Are you open to changing the way you eat to reduce your carbon footprint? Why or why not?

Food for thought

Chapter 5: What Is the Earth Serving Up?

1. Do you consider where your food comes from when you eat it—in other words, whether it comes from the earth or from a package?

2. Did you realize that the earth serves up so many different whole foods? Are you taking advantage of the earth's bounty?

3. How many of the fruits named in this chapter have you tried? How many do you eat regularly?

4. How many of the vegetables named in this chapter have you tried? How many do you eat regularly?

5. How many types of whole grains have you tried? How many do you eat regularly?

6. How many types of legumes have you tried? How many do you eat regularly?

7. How many types of nuts have you tried? How many do you eat regularly?

8. How many types of seeds have you tried? How many do you eat regularly?

9. How many types of herbs and spices have you tried? How many do you use regularly? Do you value them for their medicinal properties?

10. Are you open to exploring the world of food that the earth provides?

Food for Thought

Chapter 6: Imperfectly Vegan

1. Which of the following terms best describes your current eating pattern?

   - Vegan: a vegetarian diet that excludes all animal products, such as meat, poultry, fish, eggs, milk, cheese, and other dairy products.

   - Lacto-vegetarian: a vegetarian diet that excludes meat, poultry, fish, and eggs but includes dairy products.

   - Lacto-ovo-vegetarian: a vegetarian diet that excludes meat, poultry, and fish but includes eggs and dairy products. Most vegetarians in the United States fall into this category.

   - Semivegetarian or flexitarian: a semivegetarian diet with a focus on vegetarian food but involving occasional consumption of meat, poultry, or fish.

2. How does the term "Imperfectly Vegan" resonate with you? Are you intrigued by it?

3. Are you open to being Imperfectly Vegan? Why or why not?

4. Visit my Facebook Page—Imperfectly Vegan—and share your comments and questions. Your input is valuable!

Food for thought

Chapter 7: Gathering Ingredients

1. Are you conscious of where your food comes from?

2. Do you appreciate the fact that the way you gather food makes a difference to your health and the planet?

3. Are you open to trying new ways of gathering food? If so, how?

4. Q: True or false: "Light" olive oil contains fewer calories than regular olive oil.

   A: False. The term "light" refers to color and taste. In fact, light olive oil contains just as many calories as regular olive oil: eighty calories per tablespoon.

5. Q: True or false: Foods labeled "organic" are healthy.

   A: False. The US Department of Agriculture's "organic" seal indicates that the food was grown without antibiotics or growth hormones in the case of animal-based foods, or without pesticides, synthetic fertilizers, bioengineering, or radiation in the case of produce and grains. The term "organic" has nothing to do with the food's nutrient content.

6. Q: True or false: A package of ground beef labeled "75% lean" is a good choice for a low-fat diet, since only 25 percent of its calories come from fat.

   A: False.

Food for thought

Chapter 8: Preparing and Serving Food

1. What kind of attitude do you have when preparing food for others? Is putting dinner on the table just another task to check off your to-do list? How can you modify this process for yourself, for those you serve, and for the sacred?

2. How do you decide what to prepare? Do you like to use recipes? Do you like to experiment with new ingredients? Do you center your meal on what is available at the time?

3. How do you set your table? Are there things that you can do to make the dining experience more inviting?

4. How do you serve your food? Do you keep your serving dishes off the dining table so that your family's appetite isn't driven by visual cues? Do you offer small servings so that your guests can request more as desired?

Food for Thought

Chapter 9: Dining Together

1. Do you give gratitude for food when eating alone? Why or why not? If so, how do you do this? If not, why not? Is there a way that you could begin practicing gratitude before eating alone?

2. Do you give gratitude for food when eating with family members? Why or why not? If so, how do you do this? If not, why not? Is there a way that you could begin practicing gratitude before eating while with others?

3. What makes it difficult for you to slow down enough to fully savor and appreciate the food you eat? What can you do differently to eat more consciously?

4. How often do you eat something that you don't really like because you don't want to hurt someone's feelings? How often do you stop at a fast-food restaurant because it seems as if it is all that's available on a road trip?

5. How often does your family gather around the table for a meal? What kinds of conversations take place? Are mealtimes rushed or relaxed? Are they pleasant? If not, what could you do to make them more so?

Chapter 10: Cleaning Up the Kitchen

We are constantly undergoing transformation, especially in regard to food.

1. What is ready, or getting ready, to die in your relationship with food:

    - The habit of adding salt to your food before tasting it?

    - Rewarding your children with unhealthy snacks?

    - Reliance on caffeine to sustain your energy levels?

    - Eating meat on a daily basis?

    - Eating while driving, working, and/or talking on the phone?

    - Eating to avoid doing other things?

    - Eating to fill an emotional void?

    - Carrying home your groceries in paper or plastic?

    - Purchasing packaged foods when alternatives are available?

    - Something else?

2. What is ready, or getting ready, to be born or to spring forth with regard to your relationship with food:

    - Tasting a new fruit or vegetable?

    - Starting to make regular visits to your local farmers' market?

    - Planting a fruit tree in your backyard?

    - Using a TowerGarden to grow produce in an environmentally sustainable manner?

- Exploring your artistic side by learning, creating, or teaching a few new dishes?
- Considering the planet when deciding what foods to eat?
- Considering alternatives to traditional fast food while traveling?
- Practicing being Imperfectly Vegan?
- Eating a meatless meal for the sake of the planet, if not for yourself?
- Taking a moment to give gratitude for your food before eating it?
- Something else?

3. What changes can you make in the way you and your family eat that would foster a healthy global community? Some examples include writing to your legislators and requesting that schools refuse to stock vending machines with snacks laden with hydrogenated fats; choosing to purchase healthy manufactured snacks for soccer, baseball, and other children's activities; and offering to bring plant-based dishes to potlucks and social functions.

4. What changes can you make in the way you and your family eat that would help heal the environment? Some examples include purchasing fewer packaged foods, eating fast food less frequently, subscribing to an organic delivery service, and replacing some meat-based meals with vegetarian alternatives.

"10 Alarming Facts About Overfishing," One Green Planet, accessed April 6, 2013, www.onegreenplanet.org/animalsandnature/10-alarming-facts-about-overfishing/.

"1.02 Billion People Hungry," Food and Agriculture Organization of the United Nations, accessed April 8, 2013, www.fao.org/news/story/en/item/20568/icode/.

"2013 World Hunger and Poverty Facts and Statistics," World Hunger Education Service, accessed March 12, 2014, www.worldhunger.org/articles/Learn/world%20hunger%20facts%202002.htm.

"Americans Aren't Eating Enough Fruits and Vegetables," accessed November 13, 2014, www.ers.usda.gov/data-products/chart-gallery/detail.aspx?chartId=49484&ref=collection.

Lisa Abend, "Slow Food: Can You Eat Well *and* Save the World?" Slow Food Sacramento, accessed October 29, 2010, http://slowfoodsacramento.com/slow-food-can-you-eat-well-and-save-the-world/.

Nathaniel Altman, *Sacred Water: The Spiritual Source of Life* (Mahwah, NJ: HiddenSpring, 2002).

"Anorexia Nervosa," Mayo Clinic, accessed April 16, 2013, www.mayoclinic.com/health/anorexia/DS00606.

A. Aris and S. Leblanc, "Maternal and fetal exposure to pesticides associated to genetically modified foods in Eastern Townships of Quebec, Canada," *Reproductive Toxicology* 31, no. 4 (2011), 528–33.

Nicholas Bakalar, "Risks: More Red Meat, More Mortality," *New York Times*, accessed March 12, 2012, http://nyti.ms/yoSDPf.

Neal Barnard, "Vegetarian Diets for Weight Loss and Management: Evidence from Clinical Trials," symposium, Sixth International Conference on Vegetarian Nutrition, February 24, 2013.

Hannah Beech, "Food Aid: Hungry for Change," *TIME*, June 14, 2007.

Laura Blue, "World Food Program: On the Front Lines of Hunger," *TIME*, June 18, 2008.

'Véronique Bouvard, et al., "Carcinogenicity of Consumption of Red and Processed Meat," Lancet Oncology, accessed November 3, 2015, www.thelancet.com/journals/lanonc/article/PIIS1470-2045(15)00444-1/fulltext.

Brian Boyce, "Trends in Farm-to-Table Form a Sociological Perspective," *Journal of the Academy of Nutrition and Dietetics* 113, no. 7 (2013): 892–8.

Lester Brown, "The New Geopolitics of Food," *Foreign Policy Food Issue*, May/June 2011, 54.

A. Carlsson-Kanyama and A. D. Gonzalez, "Potential Contributions of Food Consumption Patterns to Climate Change," *American Journal of Clinical Nutrition* 89, no. 5 (2009): 1704S–9S.

Suman Chandra et al., "Assessment of Total Phenolic and Flavonoid Content, Antioxidant Properties, and Yield of Aeroponically and Conventionally Grown Leafy Vegetables and Fruit Crops: A Comparative Study," *Evidence-Based Complementary and Alternative Medicine*, 2014, http://dx.doi.org/10.1155/2014/253875.

John Cloud, "My Search for the Perfect Apple: Should It Be Organic? Should It Be Locally Grown? Making Sense of Food in 2007," *TIME*, March 12, 2007.

John Cloud, "The Myth About Exercise," *TIME*, August 17, 2009.

John Cloud, "Why Your DNA Isn't Your Destiny," *TIME*, January 18, 2010.

Alisha Coleman-Jensen et al., "Household Food Security in the United States in 2011," United States Department of Agriculture Economic Research Service (ERR-141) (September 2012): 1–37.

Richard Corliss, "Should You Be a Vegetarian? Millions of Americans Are Going Meatless. Is That a Healthy Thing?" *TIME*, July 15, 2002.

"Dear Dr. Pam: Why Doesn't Eating Lower-Fat Animal Foods Reduce Cholesterol?" *Dr. Pam Popper's Healthy News You Can Use*, accessed February 27, 2012, www.wellnessforum.com/Newsletters/NewsYouCanUse120227.pdf.

C. de Graaf and F. Kok, "Slow Food, Fast Food, and the Control of Food Intake," *Nature Reviews Endocrinology* 6, no. 5 (2010): 290–3.

Dickson Despommier, *The Vertical Farm* (New York: Thomas Dunne Books, 2010).

"Dietary Fatty Acids—Position of the American Dietetic Association and Dietitians of Canada," *Academy of Nutrition and Dietetics* 107, no. 9 (2007): 1599–1611.

"Dietary Guidelines for Americans," DietaryGuidelines.gov, accessed April 10, 2013, www.health.gov/dietaryguidelines.

"Digestive Disorders Health Center," WebMD, accessed June 14, 2013, www.webmd.com/digestive-disorders/picture-of-the-liver.

Richard Dobbs, Corinne Sawers, Fraser Thompson, et al., "Overcoming Obesity: An Initial Economic Analysis," McKinsey Global Institute, November 2014, www.mckinsey.com/insights/economic_studies/how_the_world_could_better_fight_obesity.

"Eat Together as a Family to Create Better Eating Habits," ADA's public relations team, October 12, 2007.

Christopher Ellison, "Religious Involvement and Subjective Well-Being," *Journal of Health and Social Behavior* 32 (1991): 80–99.

G. Eshel et al., "Diet, Energy, and Global Warming," *Earth Interactions* 10 (2006): 13–14.

Bonnie Farmer, "Plant-Based Diet Pattern, Plant Foods, and Weight Control: Observations from NHANES," symposium, Sixth International Conference on Vegetarian Nutrition, February 24, 2013.

M. F. K. Fisher, *The Art of Eating* (New York: Macmillan General Reference, A Simon & Schuster Macmillan Co., 1990).

Matthew Fox, *Originally Blessed* (Golden, CO: Creation Spirituality Communities, 2008).

"Food and Nutrition Professionals Can Implement Practices to Conserve Natural Resources and Support Ecological Sustainability," *Journal of the American Dietetic Association* 107, no. 6 (2007): 1033–43.

"Food Symbolism During Chinese New Year Celebrations," *Nations Online*, accessed May 12, 2014, www.nationsonline.org/oneworld/Chinese_Customs/food_symbolism.htm.

Gary Fraser, "Updates from the Adventist Health Study 2," symposium, "Epidemiological Studies of Vegetarians," Sixth International Conference on Vegetarian Nutrition, February 24, 2013.

"FTC Launches 'Operation Big Fat Lie,'" Federal Trade Commission Protecting American Consumers, accessed November 9, 2012, www.ftc.gov/news-events/press-releases/2004/11/ftc-launches-big-fat-lie-initiative-targeting-bogus-weight-loss.

"Functional Foods," *Journal of the Academy of Nutrition and Dietetics* 109, no. 4 (2009): 735–46.

"Gaia (mythology)," Wikipedia, accessed March 8, 2014, http://en.wikipedia.org/wiki/Gaia_(mythology).

Andrea G. Giancoli, "Understanding Animal Welfare Certifications: When It Comes to the

Humane Treatment of Animals, Consumer Conscience Is Leading Industry Innovation," *American Academy of Nutrition and Dietetics Food and Nutrition* magazine (January/February 2013): 12–13.

K. Glanz et al., "How Major Restaurant Chains Plan Their Menus: The Role of Profit, Demand, and Health," *American Journal of Preventive Medicine* 32, no. 5 (2007): 383–88.

"The Global Warming Survival Guide," *TIME*, April 9, 2007.

"Go Natural: Chef Alice Waters Urges a Switch from Fast Food to a Fresh, Seasonal Cuisine," *TIME*, October 30, 2005.

Eben Harrell, "CARE Turns Down U.S. Food Aid," *TIME*, August 15, 2007.

Robert Hazen, *The Story of Earth: The First 4.5 Billion Years, from Stardust to Living Planet* (New York: Penguin Group, 2012).

"Health Implications of Dietary Fiber," *Academy of Nutrition and Dietetics* 108, no. 10 (2008): 1716–31.

Melanie D. Hingle et al., "Optimism and Diet Quality in the Women's Health Initiative," *Journal of the American Dietetic Association* 114, no. 4 (2014): 1036–45.

David Holben, "Position of the American Dietetic Association: Food Insecurity in the United States," *Journal of the American Dietetic Association* 110, no. 9 (2010): 1368–77.

Erica Holt et al., "Fruit and Vegetable Consumption and Its Relation to Markers of Inflammation and Oxidative Stress in Adolescents," *Journal of the American Dietetic Association* 109, no. 3 (2009): 414–21.

"How to Fend Off a Food Craving: New Research Challenges the 'Body Knows What It Needs' Theory; Where Men Differ from Women," *Wall Street Journal*, accessed September 17, 2012, http://online.wsj.com/article/SB10000872396 390443995604578002253859884598.html.

"Hunger in America: 2014 United States Hunger and Poverty Facts," World Hunger Education Service, accessed March 13, 2014, www.worldhunger.org/articles/Learn/us_hunger_facts.htm.

"Is 2014 the Year of the Vegan?" One Green Planet, accessed January 18, 2014, www.onegreenplanet.org/news/is-2014-the-year-of-the-vegan/.

Walter Jehne, "The Biology of Global Warming and Its Profitable Mitigation," *Nature and Society* (December 2006–January 2007): 7–14.

Yu Jiang et al., "Cruciferous Vegetable Intake Is Inversely Correlated with Circulating Levels of Proinflammatory Markers in Women," *Journal of the Academy of Nutrition and Dietetics* 114, no. 5 (2014): 700–8.

Gail Perry Johnson, *The Social Cause Diet: Stories of Satisfying Acts of Service* (Lafayette, CA: Cupola Press, 2008).

Susan Kano, *Making Peace with Food* (New York: HarperCollins Publishers, 1989).

David L. Katz, JuicePlus+ Annual Conference, Yale University Prevention Research Center, spring 2012.

Joseph Keon, *Whitewash: The Disturbing Truth About Cow's Milk and Your Health* (Gabriola Island, BC: New Society Publishers, 2010).

Tim Key, "Updates from the EPIC-Oxford Study," symposium, Sixth International Conference on Vegetarian Nutrition, February 24, 2013.

Kathleen Kingsbury, "The Changing Face of Breast Cancer," *TIME*, October 15, 2007.

Jeffrey Kluger, Christine Gorman, and Alice Park, "America's Obesity Crisis: Eating Behavior: Why We Eat," *TIME*, June 7, 2004.

Jeffrey Kluger, "What Now? A Feverish Planet Badly Needs a Cure," *TIME*, April 9, 2007.

Jeffrey Kluger, "The War on Delicious," TIME, November 9, 2015.

Jeffrey Kluger, "What's So Great About Organic Food?" *TIME*, August 25, 2010.

Karin Kratina, Nancy L. King, and Dayle Hayes, *Moving Away from Diets: New Ways to Heal Eating Problems & Exercise Resistance* (Lake Dallas, TX: Helm Publishing, 1999).

Mark Kurlansky, "The Food Chains That Link Us All," *TIME*, June 14, 2007.

Helena H. LaRoche et al., "Changes in Diet Behavior when Adults Become Parents," *Journal of the American Dietetic Association* 112, no. 6 (2012): 832–8.

Claus Leitzmann, "Vegetarian Diet: Past, Present, and the Future," plenary address, Sixth International Conference on Vegetarian Nutrition, February 25, 2013.

"Long Live the Mediterranean Diet," *UC Berkeley Wellness Letter*, March 2014, 3.

J. I. Macdiarmid, J. Kyle, G. W. Horgan, et al., "Sustainable Diets for the Future: Can We Contribute to Reducing Greenhouse Gas Emissions by Eating a Healthy Diet?" *American Journal of Clinical Nutrition* 96, no. 3 (2012): 632–9.

Krista Mahr, "Food Prices: Up, Up, and Away," *TIME*, February 04, 2011.

Reed Mangels, Virginia Messina, and Mark Messina, *The Dietitian's Guide to Vegetarian Diets: Issues and Applications, Third Edition* (Sudbury, MA: Jones & Bartlett Learning, 2011).

Marilynn Marchione, "Fat kids found to have arteries of 45-year-olds," Associated Press, accessed November 11, 2008, www.highbeam.com/doc/1A1-D94D0VNG0.html.

Sheldon Margen, *The Wellness Encyclopedia of Food and Nutrition* (New York, NY: Rebus, 1992).

Mac Margolis, "10 Big Green Ideas: Make a Greener Burger," *Newsweek*, October 25, 2010.

M. G. Marmot and S. L. Syme, "Acculturation and Coronary Heart Disease in Japanese-Americans," *American Journal of Epidemiology* 204 (1976): 22–47.

Gabriel Masset et al., *Journal of the American Dietetic Association*, 114, no. 6 (2014): 862–9.

Richard Mattes, "Nut Consumption: Accessibility, Satiety, and Metabolism," symposium, Sixth International Conference on Vegetarian Nutrition, February 24, 2013.

Matthew 13:31–32, The Bible, New International Version.

A. J. McMichael et al., "Food, Livestock Production, Energy Climate Change, and Health," *Lancet* 370 (2007): 1253–63.

Thomas McNamee, *Alice Waters and Chez Panisse* (New York: Penguin Books, 2008).

Meredith Melnick, "Fast Food's Biggest Customer: Not the Poor, but the Middle Class," *TIME*, November 7, 2011.

Meredith Melnick, "Study: Fast-Food Ads Target Kids with Unhealthy Food, and It Works," *TIME*, November 8, 2010.

Meredith Melnick, "The Sad State of American Kids' Food Environments," *TIME*, April 28, 2011.

Meredith Melnick, "The USDA Ditches the Food Pyramid for a Plate," *TIME*, June 2, 2011.

Virginia Messina, "Research in Vegetarian Nutrition: Trends and Highlights from the Past 20 Years," *Vegetarian Nutrition Update* 21, no. 1 (2012): 1–4.

G. E. Miller, "Frugality Through Vegetarianism: How to Save $2–$3K Per Year & the Planet by Moving Away from a Meat-Based Diet," 20 Something Finance, accessed January 5, 2104, http://20somethingfinance.com/cost-of-vegetarian-diet/.

D. J. Millward and T. Garnett, "Food and the Planet: Nutritional Dilemmas of Greenhouse Gas Emission Reductions Through Reduced Intakes of Meat and Dairy Foods," *Proceedings of the Nutrition Society* 69, no. 1 (2010): 103–18.

David A. Mortensen et al., "Navigating a Critical Juncture for Sustainable Weed Management," *BioScience* 62 (2012): 75–84.

National Center for Health Statistics, "Health, United States, 2011: With Special Feature on Socioeconomic Status and Health," accessed March 12, 2012, www.cdc.gov/nchs/data/hus/hus11.pdf#022.

"National Vital Statistics Report," Centers for Disease Control, accessed April 15, 2014, www.cdc.gov/nchs/data/nvsr/nvsr60/nvsr60_04.pdf.

Marion Nestle, *Food Politics, How the Food Industry Influences Nutrition and Health* (Berkeley and Los Angeles: University of CA Press, 2002, 2007).

Marion Nestle, *What to Eat* (New York: North Point Press, 2006).

Jack Norris and Virginia Messina, *Vegan for Life* (Boston: Da Capo Press, 2011).

"Nut," *Jewish Encyclopedia*, accessed May 8, 2014, www.jewishencyclopedia.com/articles/11635-nut.

"Nutrient Supplementation," *Academy of Nutrition and Dietetics* 109, no. 12 (2009): 2073–85.

"Nuts and Seeds: Ancient Foods That Are Still Nutritional Gems Today," North American Vegetarian Society, accessed May 8, 2014, www.navsonline.org/nutrition/healthfulfoods/nutsandseeds.php.

Oldham-Cooper et al., "Playing a Computer Game During Lunch Affects Fullness, Memory for Lunch, and Later Snack Intake," *American Journal of Clinical Nutrition* 93, no. 2 (2011): 308–13.

Dean Ornish, *Dr. Dean Ornish's Program for Reversing Heart Disease: The Only System Scientifically Proven to Reverse Heart Disease Without Drugs or Surgery* (New York: Ivy Books, 1995).

Michael D. K. Owen, "Weed Resistance Development and Management in Herbicide-Tolerant Crops: Experiences from the USA," *Journal of Consumer Protection and Food Safety* 1 (2011): 85–9.

A. Pan, Q. Sun, A. M. Bernstein, et al., "Red Meat Consumption and Mortality: Results form 2 Prospective Cohort Studies," *Archives of Internal Medicine* 172, no. 7 (2012): 555–63.

Alice Park, "How to Live 100 Years," *TIME*, February 22, 2010.

Annie Murphy Paul, "How the First Nine Months Shape the Rest of Your Life," *TIME*, October 4, 2010.

Stacy Perman, "The Joy of Not Cooking: Americans Spend Less Time Cooking Every Year. Yet the $100 Billion Home-Meal Replacement Market has Produced Few Winners," *TIME*, June 1, 1998.

Carlo Petrini, *Slow Food Nation: Why Our Food Should Be Good, Clean, and Fair* (New York: Rizzoli International Publications, 2007).

Kate Pickert, "Fast Food's Secret Ingredient: Corn," *TIME*, November 14, 2008.

Kate Pickert, "Local-Food Maven Alice Waters," *TIME*, March 25, 2009.

David Pimentel and Marcia Pimentel, "Sustainability of Meat-Based and Plant-Based Diets and the Environment," *American Journal of Clinical Nutrition* 78, no. 3 (2003): 660S–3S.

Elizabeth Pivonka et al., "Development of the Behaviorally Focused Fruits & Veggies—More Matters Public Health Initiative," *Journal of the American Dietetic Association* 111, no. 10 (2011): 1570–7.

"Michael Pollan: A Plant's Eye View," TED Talks, accessed September 21, 2012, www.ted.com/talks/michael_pollan_gives_a_plant_s_eye_view.

Michael Pollan, *The Omnivore's Dilemma: A Natural History of Four Meals* (New York: Penguin, 2006).

Mary Pols, "*Food, Inc.* Takes a Critical Look at the American Food Industry. Don't Despair—There's Hope," *TIME*, June 22, 2009.

Pamela Popper, *Solving America's Healthcare Crisis* (Worthington, OH: PB Industries, 2010).

Mitra Ray and Jennifer Daniels, *Do You Have the Guts to Be Beautiful?* (Seattle, WA: Shining Star Publishing, 2008).

Monica Reinagel, "Not Your Mother's Spice Cabinet," *American Academy of Nutrition and Dietetics Food and Nutrition* magazine (spring 2012): 14–7.

Linda Riebel, *The Green Foodprint* (Lafayette, CA: Print & Pixel Books, 2011).

Bonnie Rochman, "Want to Know My Future?" *TIME*, December 24, 2012.

Brandi Y. Rollins et al., "The Beneficial Effect of Family Meals on Obesity Differs by Race, Sex, and Household Education: The National Survey of Children's Health, 2003–2004," *Journal of the American Dietetic Association* 110, no. 9 (2010): 1335–9.

Margot Roosevelt, "Fresh Off the Farm: A New Breed of Planters and Eaters Are Joining Fores to Nurture the Local-Foods Movement," *TIME*, November 3, 2003.

Sharon Ross, "Nutrigenomics, Plant-Based Dietary Patterns, and Cancer," symposium, Sixth International Conference on Vegetarian Nutrition, February 25, 2013.

Richard Rudd, *Gene Keys: Unlocking the Higher Purpose Hidden in Your DNA* (London: Watkins Publishing, 2013).

Joan Sabate, *Vegetarian Nutrition* (Boca Raton, FL: CRC Press, 2001).

Jordi Salad-Salvado, "Nuts in the Prevention and Treatment of Cardio Metabolic Syndrome," symposium, Sixth International Conference on Vegetarian Nutrition, February 24, 2013.

P. Scarborough et al., "Modelling the Health Impact of Environmentally Sustainable Dietary Scenarios in the UK," *European Journal of Clinical Nutrition* 66, no. 6 (2012): 710–15.

Julie T. Schaefer and Amy B. Magnuson, "A Review of Interventions That Promote Eating by Internal Cues," *Journal of the American Dietetic Association* 114, no. 5 (2014): 734–60.

Helen Schucman and William Thetford, *A Course In Miracles* (Tiburon, CA: Foundation for Inner Peace, 1985).

Michael Schuman, "Is Another Food Crisis Coming?" *TIME*, August 11, 2010.

Michael Schuman, "Population Growth Has Driven Up the Food Price to Alarming Levels," *TIME*, July 14, 2011.

"The Science of Living Longer," *TIME*, February 22, 2010.

Gilles-Éric Séralini et al., "Genetically Modified Crops Safety Assessments: Present Limits and Possible Improvements," *Environmental Sciences* 23 (2011): 10.

Meena Shah et al., "Slower Eating Speed Lowers Energy Intake in Normal-Weight but not Overweight/Obese Subjects," *Journal of the American Dietetic Association* 114, no. 3 (2014): 393–402.

Vandana Shiva, *Stolen Harvest: The Hijacking of the Global Food Supply* (Cambridge, MA: South End Press, 2000).

Eric Shlosser, *Fast Food Nation* (New York: Penguin Press, 2002).

B. H. Singer and C. D. Ryff, eds., *New Horizons in Health: An Integrative Approach*, National Research Council (US) Committee on Future Directions for Behavioral and Social Sciences Research at the National Institutes of Health (Washington, DC: National Academies Press, 2001), accessed July 12, 2012, www.ncbi.nlm.nih.gov/books/NBK43780/.

Pramil Singh, "Obesity Trends in a Vegetarian Subcontinent: India," symposium, Sixth International Conference on Vegetarian Nutrition, February 24, 2013.

Sora Song, "Are Cartoon Characters Coaxing Kids to Eat Junk Food?" *TIME*, June 21, 2010.

"The State of Food Insecurity in the World," Food and Agricultural Organization, accessed March 12, 2014, www.fao.org/docrep/005/y7352e/y7352e00.htm.

E. Stehfest, L. Bouwman, D. P. van Vuuren, et al., "Climate Benefits of Changing Diet," *Climate Change* 95, nos. 1–2 (2009): 83–102.

Joel Stein, "The Fast-Food Ethicist: At His Chipotle Restaurants, Steve Ells Serves Pasture-Raised Pork Burritos and Antibiotic-Free Chicken Tacos. It's Paying Off," *TIME*, July 23, 2012.

Henning Steinfeld, *Livestock's Long Shadow: Environmental Issues and Options* (Rome, Italy: Food and Agricultural Organization, 2006).

M. P. Stern et al., "Secular Decline in Death Rates Due to Ischemic Heart Disease in Mexican Americans and Non-Hispanic Whites in Texas, 1970–1980," *Circulation* 76 (1987): 1245–50.

Carina Storrs, "Study Questions the Link Between Food Environment and Diet Quality," *TIME*, July 15, 2011.

Tristram Stuart, "The Global Food Waste Scandal," TED Talks, accessed September 21, 2012, www.youtube.com/watch?v=cWC_zDdF74s.

Erin Sund, "The Urban Farm: A New American Frontier," *American Academy of Nutrition and Dietetics Food and Nutrition* magazine (March/April 2013): 12–13.

John Swartzberg et al., "Do Cholesterol Numbers Still Matter? New Guidelines Include the Most Dramatic—and Controversial—Changes in 25 Years," *University of California Berkeley Wellness Letter*, 2014.

John Swartzberg et al., "The Wellness Reports: Controlling Your Cholesterol—Your No-Nonsense Guide to Staying Well," *University of California Berkeley Wellness Letter*, 2015.

John Swartzberg et al., "The Wellness Reports: Dietary Supplements—Your Complete Guide to Making the Best Choices," *University of California Berkeley Wellness Letter*, 2014.

John Swartzberg et al., "The Wellness Reports: Eating for Optimal Health—Your No-Nonsense Guide to Staying Well," *University of California Berkeley Wellness Letter*, 2015.

John Swartzberg et al., "The Wellness Reports: Men's Health—Your No-Nonsense Guide to Staying Well," *University of California Berkeley Wellness Letter*, 2014.

John Swartzberg et al., "The Wellness Reports: Women's Health—Your No-Nonsense Guide to Staying Well," *University of California Berkeley Wellness Letter*, 2015.

S. L. Syme et al., "Some Social and Cultural Factors Associated with the Occurrence of Coronary Heart Disease," *Journal of Chronic Disease* 82 (1965): 334–46.

S. L. Syme et al., "Epidemiologic Studies of Coronary Heart Disease and Stroke in Japanese Men Living in Japan, Hawaii, and California," *American Journal of Epidemiology* 102 (1975): 477–80.

Ibid., 481–90.

Ibid., 514–25.

S. L. Syme, Chapter 6: "Control and Health: An Epidemiological Perspective," in K. W. Schaie, *Self-Directedness* (Hillside, NJ: Erbaum, 1989), 213–29.

S. L. Syme and L. F. Berkman, "Social Class, Susceptibility, and Sickness," *American Journal of Epidemiology* 104 (1976): 31–73.

Gary Taubes, "When I Grow Up, I'm Going to Weigh 300 Lbs. Help!" *Newsweek*, May 14, 2012.

"Tackling America's Eating Habits, One Store at a Time," *Disease Prevention*, accessed October 8, 2012, www.sciencemag.org/content/337/6101/1466.full.pdf?sid=67d11237-76b4-486e-a628-0fb16f6ebea6.

"Global Diets Link Environmental Sustainability and Human Health," *Nature*, accessed November 21, 2014, www.ncbi.nlm.nih.gov/pubmed/25383533.

"Top Hunger Organizations: Learn About the Organizations Striving to End Food Insecurity Worldwide," *Academy of Nutrition and Dietetics Food and Nutrition Magazine* (September/October 2013): 9–11.

"The Truth About Eating Animals," People for the Ethical Treatment of Animals, accessed April 6, 2013, www.mediapeta.com/peta/Images/Global/peta_infographic-truthabouteating.jpg.

A. Tukker, G. Huppes, J. Guinée, et al., "Environmental Impact of Products (EIPRO): Analysis of the Life Cycle Environmental Impacts Related to the Total Final Consumption of the EU 25" (Seville, Spain: European Commission DG Joint Research Centre, 2006).

Brad Tuttle, "Why We're Eating Fewer Happy Meals," *TIME*, April 23, 2012.

Catherine Upin and John Hockenberry, "Climate of Doubt," *Frontline* transcript, accessed October 24, 2012, www.pbs.org/wgbh/pages/frontline/environment/climate-of-doubt/transcript-31/.

"Use of Nutritive and Nonnutritive Sweeteners," *Journal of the Academy of Nutrition and Dietetics* 112, no. 5 (2012): 739–58.

"Vegetable Myth and Folklore," squidoo, accessed May 12, 2014, www.squidoo.com/vegetable-myths.

"Vegetarian Diets," *Journal of the Academy of Nutrition and Dietetics* 109, no. 7 (2009): 1266–82.

"Vegetarianism in America," *Vegetarian Times*, accessed January 18, 2014, www.vegetariantimes.com/article/vegetarianism-in-america.

"Vegetarian Lifestyle," Academy of Nutrition and Dietetics, accessed October 10, 2012, www.eatright.org/Public/content.aspx?id=6372#.UHG8q44eFH0.

Melina Vesanto and Brenda Davis, *The New Becoming Vegetarian* (Summertown, TN: Healthy Living Publications, 2003).

"Vitamins: How Many Americans Use Them?" *Huffington Post*, accessed June 2, 2014, www.huffingtonpost.com/2011/04/13/vitamin-use_n_848777.html.

Helen C. Wagenvoord, "The High Price of Cheap Food," *San Francisco Chronicle* magazine, May 2, 2004.

Barbara G. Walker, *The Woman's Encyclopedia of Myths and Secrets* (San Francisco: HarperCollins Publishers, 1983).

Bryan Walsh, "America's Food Crisis and How to Fix It," *TIME*, August 31, 2009.

Bryan Walsh, "Diet: Eat Your Greens" *TIME*, February 23, 2009.

Bryan Walsh, "Feeding the Planet Without Destroying It," *TIME*, May 22, 2012.

Bryan Walsh, "Foodies Can Eclipse (and Save) the Green Movement," *TIME*, February 15, 2011.

Bryan Walsh, "The End of the Line: Fish Are the Last Wild Food, but Our Oceans Are Being Picked Clean. Can Farming Fish Take the Place of Catching Them?" *TIME*, July 18, 2011.

Bryan Walsh, "The Morality of Mealtime," *TIME*, March 30, 2011.

Bryan Walsh, "The Real Cost of Cheap Food," *TIME*, August 31, 2009.

Vivienne Walt, "Food Prices: Hunger Strikes," *TIME*, June 5, 2008.

Pam Warhurst, "How Can We Eat Our Landscapes?" TED Talks, accessed August 10, 2012, www.youtube.com/watch?v=4KmKoj4RSZw.

W. C. Willett, "Diet and Health: What Should We Eat?" *Science* 22 (April 1994): 532–7.

"What Is Heart Rate? What is a Normal Pulse Rate?" MNT Knowledge Center, accessed June 14, 2013, www.medicalnewstoday.com/articles/235710.php

R. Whelan, *Self-Reliance: The Wisdom of Ralph Waldo Emerson* (New York: Bell Tower, 1991).

Women, Infants, and Children (WIC) United States Department of Agriculture Food and Nutrition Service, accessed April 15, 2013, www.fns.usda.gov/wic.

"Your Kidneys and How They Work," WebMD, accessed June 14, 2013, www.webmd.com/a-to-z-guides/function-kidneys.

Yong Zhu and James Hollis, "Increasing the Number of Chews Before Swallowing Reduces Meal Size in Normal-Weight, Overweight, and Obese Adults," *Journal of the Academy of Nutrition and Dietetics* 114, no. 6 (2014): 926–31.

Richard Zoglin, "Food: Fast Food Speeds up the Pace," *TIME*, June 21, 2005.

Lello Zolla et al., "Proteomics as a Complementary Tool for Identifying Unintended Side Effects Occurring in Transgenic Maize Seeds as a Result of Genetic Modifications," *Journal of Proteome Research* 7 (2009): 1850–61.

Resources

BOOKS

Being Vegetarian for Dummies
Suzanne Havala, MS, RD (Cleveland, OH: IDG Books Worldwide, 2001)

Summary: This book provides an easy-to-understand look at vegetarian diets, including nutrition issues; practical tips, menu planning, and recipe modification; pregnancy; infants, children, and teens; and athletes.

Simply Vegan: Quick Vegetarian Meals, Third Edition
Debra Wasserman; nutrition section by Reed Mangels, PhD, RD (Baltimore, MD: the Vegetarian Resource Group, 1999)

Summary: This book features a nutrition section that briefly discusses key nutrients in the vegan diet. It also includes over 160 quick-and-easy recipes.

The Vegetarian Way: Total Health for You and Your Family
Virginia Messina, MPH, RD, and Mark Messina, PhD (New York: Crown Trade Paperbacks, 1996)

Summary: This authoritative and comprehensive handbook provides information on all aspects of vegetarian nutrition, including nutrient sources and nutritional needs for vegetarians of all ages. Includes recipes, menus, food guides, and cooking tips.

Vegan for Life
Jack Norris and Virginia Messina (Boston, MA: Da Capo Press, 2011)

Summary: This outstanding guide to vegan diets thoroughly covers basic nutrition topics for vegans, provides a vegan food guide; addresses the needs of children and pregnant women; and discusses topics like being overweight, eating disorders, and vegan athletes.

Vegan & Vegetarian FAQ: Answers to Your Frequently Asked Questions
Davida Gypsy Breier; nutrition section by Reed Mangels, PhD, RD (Baltimore, MD: the Vegetarian Resource Group, 2001)

Summary: This book provides hundreds of answers on everything from food ingredients to vegetarian nutrition to vegetarian cooking.

MAGAZINES, NEWSLETTERS, AND PAMPHLETS

Loma Linda University Vegetarian Nutrition & Health Letter
Website: www.llu.edu/llu/vegetarian (includes

selected articles from previous issues and subscription information)

Summary: This newsletter is published ten times per year by Loma Linda University. It provides information about the latest scientific developments in vegetarian nutrition, as well as information about vegetarian foods and cooking.

"Position of the American Dietetic Association: Vegetarian Diets"
American Dietetic Association (ADA)

Website: www.eatright.org/cps/rde/xchg/ada/hs.xsl/advocacy_933_ENU_HTML.htm

PDF version: www.eatright.org/ada/files/veg.pdf

Summary: The American Dietetic Association's position paper on vegetarian nutrition. This technical paper includes a food guide pyramid for vegetarian meal planning and a table of food sources of key nutrients.

"Vegetarianism in a Nutshell"; "Veganism in a Nutshell"
The Vegetarian Resource Group

Web versions: www.vrg.org/nutshell/nutshell.htm; www.vrg.org/nutshell/vegan.htm

Summary: These pamphlets contain basic information on vegetarian and vegan nutrition and foods.

Vegetarian Journal
Website: www.vrg.org/journal (includes selected articles from previous issues and subscription information)

Summary: This quarterly magazine is published by the Vegetarian Resource Group. It includes practical tips for vegetarian meal planning, articles relevant to vegetarian nutrition, recipes, and natural-food-product reviews.

FACEBOOK PAGES

Imperfectly Vegan

The Sacred Art of Eating

Mercy for Animals

Plant-Based Dietitian

The Vegan RD

ORGANIZATIONS TO CONSIDER SUPPORTING

A Vegetarian's Guide to Healthy Eating
Wegmans Food Markets, Inc.

Website: www.wegmans.com/eatwelllivewell/healthyEating/introduction.asp

Summary: Provides information on vegetarian diets, including key nutrients, cooking and shopping tips, FAQs, and life-cycle issues.

Food Guides
Nutrispeak, Vesanto Melina, RD

Website: www.nutrispeak.com/foodguides.htm

Summary: Vegan and Vegetarian Pyramids, based on the U.S. Food Guide, and the Vegan Rainbow and the Vegetarian Rainbow, based on the Canadian Food Guide.

Health and Nutrition
The Vegetarian Society of the United Kingdom

Website: www.vegsoc.org/health

Summary: This site includes a very complete listing of resources and fact sheets on many aspects of vegetarian nutrition, including basic nutrition, protein, fats and cholesterol, calcium, iron, vitamin B_{12}, and zinc.

Plant-Based Diets: Fact and Fiction
Seventh-Day Adventist Dietetic Association

Website: www.sdada.org/plant.htm

Summary: Myths and realities of a vegetarian diet.

Staying Healthy on Plant-Based Diets

Website: www.veganhealth.org/sh

Summary: Well-referenced collection of nutrition information for vegans. Includes information on health benefits, meal planning ideas, and nutritional issues of which vegans should be aware, focusing on recommended daily intakes of important nutrients.

"Update on Calcium: Do Vegetarians Need Less?"
Loma Linda University Vegetarian Nutrition & Health Letter, February 1999.

Website: www.llu.edu/llu/vegetarian/calcium.htm

Summary: This article provides information on calcium needs of vegetarians and good sources of calcium.

Vegan Outreach

Website: www.veganoutreach.org/whyvegan/health.html

Vegan RD

Website: www.theveganrd.com

Summary: Well-researched responses to questions about all aspects of vegetarian nutrition and foods. Written by Virginia Messina, MPH, RD, and updated weekly.

Vegetarian Basics 101
Vegetarians in Paradise: A Los Angeles Vegetarian Monthly Web Magazine

Website: www.vegparadise.com

Summary: Provides information on types of vegetarians, getting started in vegetarianism, foods, protein sources, and benefits of vegetarianism

Vegetarian Diets
American Heart Association

Website: http://216.185.112.5/presenter.jhtml?identifier=4777

Summary: Defines different types of vegetarianism and provides nutritional information related to vegetarian diets.

Vegetarian Food Guide
Loma Linda University

Website: www.llu.edu/llu/nutrition/vegguide.html

Summary: Vegetarian food guide pyramid and supporting information, including principles of healthful vegetarian diets.

Vegetarian Nutrition
Food and Nutrition Information Center, USDA

Website: www.nal.usda.gov/fnic/etext/000058.html

Summary: Links to web resources on many aspects of vegetarianism.

Vegetarian Resource Group

Website: www.vrg.org

Summary: This website contains a wealth of information on vegetarian nutrition—including nutrients like iron, calcium, protein, and vitamin B_{12}—as well as reprints of nutrition-related articles from *Vegetarian Journal*.

What Every Vegan Should Know about Vitamin B_{12}
The Vegan Society

Website: www.vegansociety.com/html/info/b12sheet.htm

Summary: Brief statement on vitamin B_{12} sources and recommendations for intake followed by an extensive technical review of information on vitamin B_{12}.

Vitamin B_{12} in the Vegan Diet
The Vegetarian Resource Group

Website: www.vrg.org/nutrition/b12.htm

Summary: Provides information on vitamin B_{12} sources and recommendations.

VEGETARIAN DIETS AND DISEASE PREVENTION/TREATMENT

Cookbooks

Cooking Vegetarian
Vesanto Mellina and Joseph Forest (Toronto: Macmillan, 1996)

Everyday Cooking with Dr. Dean Ornish: 150 Easy, Low-Fat, High-Flavor Recipes
Dean Ornish, MD (New York: HarperCollins, 1997)

Forks over Knives—the Cookbook: Over 300 Recipes for Plant-Based Eating All Through the Year
Del Sroufe, Julieanna Hever, Isa Chandra Moskowitz, and Darshana Thacker (2012)

Joy of Cooking: All About Vegetarian Cooking
Irma S. Rombauer, Marion Rombauer Becker, Ethan Becker (New York: Scribner, 2000)

Lorna Sass' Complete Vegetarian Kitchen: Where Good Flavors and Good Health Meet
Lorna Sass (New York: William Morrow & Co., 2002)

Madhur Jaffrey's World Vegetarian
Madhur Jaffrey (New York: Random House, 2002).

Meatless Meals for Working People: Quick and Easy Vegetarian Recipes, Fourth Edition
Debra Wasserman and Charles Stahler (Baltimore, MD: the Vegetarian Resource Group, 2004)

Moosewood Restaurant New Classics
Moosewood Collective (New York: Clarkson Potter, 2001).

More Soy of Cooking: Healthful Renditions of Classic Traditional Meals
Marie Oser (New York: John Wiley & Sons, 2000)

Soy Desserts: 101 Fun and Fabulously Healthy Recipes
Patricia Greenberg (New York: Regan Books, 2000)

The Complete Soy Cookbook
Paulette Mitchell (New York: Macmillan, 1998)

The Gluten-Free Vegan
Susan O'Brien (Philadelphia: Da Capo Press, 2007)

The New Moosewood Cookbook
Mollie Katzen (Berkeley, CA: Ten Speed Press, 2000)

The Vegetarian 5-Ingredient Gourmet
Nava Atlas (New York: Broadway Books, 2001)

The Vegetarian Gourmet's Easy International Recipes
Bobbie Hinman (Chicago: Surrey Books, 2001)

Vegan Meals for One or Two
Nancy Berkoff, RD (Baltimore, MD: the Vegetarian Resource Group, 2001)

Vegetarian Cooking for Dummies
Suzanne Havala, MS, RD (New York: Hungry Minds, 2001)

Vegetarian Cooking for Everyone
Deborah Madison (New York: Broadway Books, 1997)

Vegetarian Times: Complete Cookbook
Editors of *Vegetarian Times* (New York: MacMillan, 1995)

JUICEPLUS+ WHOLE-FOOD SUPPLEMENTATION

www.juiceplus.com

www.childrenshealthstudy.com

www.transform30.com

www.towergarden.com

OTHER RECOMMENDED READING

Dickson Despommier, *The Vertical Farm* (New York: Thomas Dunne Books, 2010).

Joseph Keon, *Whitewash: The Disturbing Truth About Cow's Milk and Your Health* (Gabriola Island, BC: New Society Publishers, 2010).

Carlo Petrini, *Slow Food Nation: Why Our Food Should Be Good, Clean, and Fair* (New York: Rizzoli International Publications, 2007).

Vandana Shiva, *Stolen Harvest: The Hijacking of the Global Food Supply* (Cambridge, MA: South End Press, 2000).

RECOMMENDED FILMS

- *King Corn*
- *Fed Up*
- *The Future of Food*
- *Forks Over Knives*
- *Cowspiracy*
- *Earthlings*
- *Fridays at the Farm*
- *Food Matters*
- *Vegicated*
- *Ingredients*
- *Super Size Me*
- *The World According to Monsanto*
- *Tapped*
- *Water: The Great Mystery*
- *Flow: For Love of Water*
- *Blue Gold: World Water Wars*

FOOD SECURITY RESOURCES ▪▪▪▪

The US Department of Agriculture's Food and Nutrition Service administers a range of nutrition assistance programs throughout the United States (www.fns.usda.gov/fsec/).

The Food Research and Action Center, a national nonprofit organization, is working to improve public policies and public-private partnerships to eradicate hunger and undernutrition in the United States (www.frac.org/index.html).

The United Nations' World Food Programme includes among its missions saving lives during refugee crises improving the nutrition and quality of life of the world's most vulnerable people, and enabling development (www.wfp.org).

The World Bank is a source of financial and technical assistance to developing countries, with the goal of reducing global poverty and improving living standards (www.worldbank.org).

The International Food Policy Research Institute provides policy solutions that reduce hunger and malnutrition throughout the world order (www.ifpri.org).

LEADING HUNGER ORGANIZATIONS ▪▪▪▪

AARP and AARP Foundation
Twitter: @AARPCares
Facebook: AARPFoundation

Feeding America
Twitter: @FeedingAmerica
Facebook: feedingamerica

Generations United
Twitter: @GensUnited
Facebook: generationsunited

Meals on Wheels
Twitter: @MealsOnWheels
Facebook: mowaa

Share Our Strength
Twitter: @nokidhungry
Facebook: nokidhungryorg

UNICEF
Twitter: @Unicefusa
Facebook: UNICEF-USA

World Food Programme
Twitter: @WFP
Facebook: WFPUSA

SPIRITUALITY ▓▓▓▓▓▓▓

Richard Rudd, *Gene Keys: Unlocking the Higher Purpose Hidden in Your DNA* (London: Watkins Publishing, 2013).

WEBSITES ▓▓▓▓▓▓▓

One Green Planet: www.onegreenplanet.org

People for the Ethical Treatment of Animals: www.PETA.org

Post Punk Kitchen: www.theppk.com

International Vegetarian Union (IVU): www.ivu.org/recipes

Vegetarians in Paradise: www.vegparadise.com

VegKitchen with Nava Atlas: www.vegkitchen.com

Vegetarian Nutrition Dietetic Practice Group: www.vegetariannutrition.net

Vegetarian Recipes: www.allrecipes.com

Vegetarian Resource Group: www.vrg.org

Vegetarian Society of the United Kingdom: www.vegsoc.org/health

Vegetarian Times: www.vegetariantimes.com

VegWeb: www.vegweb.com

❧

About the Author

LISA TREMONT OTA, RD, MPH, MA

A registered dietitian and public health nutritionist with degrees in nutrition and spirituality, Lisa is uniquely qualified to help us understand our dynamic relationship with food. In 1987, she graduated from UC Berkeley with a bachelor of science in nutrition and clinical dietetics and received the Nutrition Sciences Departmental Citation Award. In 1990, she earned a master's degree in public health nutrition, with high honors, from UC Berkeley. In 1996, she obtained a master's degree in culture and creation spirituality from Holy Names College. Lisa's passion for the unbreakable links between food and spirituality is the result of more than twenty years of academic, professional, and personal exploration.

Recognizing that prevention is more efficient than treatment, Lisa has developed wellness programs for various nonprofit organizations, governmental agencies, and corporations, including Safeway and Pacific Bell. She directed the first California-wide distribution of UC Berkeley's *Wellness Guide* to more than one million English- and Spanish-speaking participants in the state's Special Supplemental Nutrition Program for Women, Infants, and Children (WIC). Over the years, she has led over one hundred grocery store tours, including one with Dr. Nancy Snyderman for KPIX Channel 5 News in San Francisco, and has appeared on KGO-TV's *The View from the Bay*.

Lisa is a member of the American Academy of Nutrition and Dietetics, a proud representative of the JuicePlus+ Company, and volunteers with the Cooking with Kids Foundation. Lisa's website (www.sacredexploration .com) and Facebook pages (The Sacred Art of Eating and Imperfectly Vegan) nourish our dynamic relationship with food in support of our individual, communal, and environmental well-being. Lisa is a native of the San Francisco Bay Area, where she resides with her family. When she's not gardening and cooking, you'll likely find her on the dance floor.

Made in the USA
Columbia, SC
17 October 2017